BASIC hydraulics

To
Elizabeth, Caroline and Rachel

BASIC hydraulics

P D Smith MA, MSc
Senior Lecturer
Civil Engineering Department
Royal Military College of Science, Shrivenham, England

Butterworth Scientific
London . Boston . Durban . Singapore . Sydney . Toronto . Wellington

First published, 1982

© Butterworth & Co (Publishers) Ltd, 1982

British Library Cataloguing in Publication Data

Smith, P.D.
  BASIC hydraulics.
  1. Basic (Computer program language)
  2. Hydraulic engineering–Data processing
  I. Title
  001.64′24   QA76.3

  ISBN 0-408-01112-2

Typeset by Scribe Design, Gillingham, Kent
Printed in England by Page Bros Ltd., Norwich, Norfolk

Preface

The importance of computers and computer programming today cannot be underestimated. The computer is a device whose field of application is growing very rapidly and one which is especially useful in science and engineering. In education, computing is now in the curriculum of all university engineering courses and it is not uncommon for sixth-formers at school to have access to small desk-top minicomputers.

Computing in universities, polytechnics and colleges, etc., often seems to be taught by computer scientists or mathematicians and this can sometimes, quite unintentionally, lead to it being isolated from the engineering subjects. This is unfortunate because there are several advantages which accrue from linking computing and engineering studies. Engineering can be a great aid to the understanding of computing methods by showing their relevance to particular aspects of the subjects and by providing exercises with which programming techniques can be learnt, practised and developed. By fostering such an inter-relation, computing is then seen to be both an essential and natural activity for engineers. The other side of the coin is that computing is seen to be a great help to engineering because a clear exposition (and consequently a good understanding) of the engineering equations and procedures is required in order to write a successful computer program.

This book uses the programming language called BASIC, an acronym derived from 'Beginner's All-purpose Symbolic Instruction Code'. With the development of microcomputers which have built-in BASIC, this language has largely usurped FORTRAN (and its variants) as the most important computer language for general use by engineers. When students write computer programs, the use of BASIC is seen to have the advantage over other languages in that it enables programs to be developed (i.e. run, modified when errors are found and then re-run until successful operation has been achieved) more rapidly than with other systems. This allows the student to complete even a quite complex exercise within a relatively short time (e.g. in a single afternoon session or study period). This in itself helps to retain the student's interest in the problem and builds up his confidence in his ability to compute successfully.

It is therefore both possible and beneficial to integrate the teaching and use of computing with his engineering studies for an undergraduate student of civil, mechanical or electrical engineering (the three areas of study with which the author has had closest contact) and the same must be true for other fields of engineering and science.

This book does not attempt to describe the subject of hydraulics in a comprehensive manner — there are many other such books available. Neither, for the self-same reason, does this work cover the BASIC language in any great detail. Rather, this book is aimed at helping students both to become proficient in BASIC by actually using the language in an important field of engineering and to use computing as a means of mastering the subject of hydraulics.

The book could equally well have been titled *BASIC Civil Engineering Fluid Mechanics* because it is primarily aimed at the first- and second-year undergraduate student of civil engineering who will be concerned with the application of fundamental fluid mechanics theory to civil engineering problems. Because of the complex nature of many of the fundamental equations of fluid mechanics which are very difficult to solve by even the most sophisticated of computer techniques, some simplification of these equations is required, together with the frequent use of empirical relationships, in order to make analysis of specific problems more tractable. Even then a certain complexity remains and the use of BASIC computer programs can greatly facilitate an understanding of the subject, as is demonstrated in the Worked Examples throughout the book.

With the exception of the first, which presents a summary of the technique of computing in BASIC together with comments and listing of the main commands and statements, each chapter consists of a short text which contains a summary of relevant theory. This is in the form of short 'essays' which introduce the fundamental concepts and the appropriate governing equations. There follows a series of worked examples consisting primarily of an introduction in which the general topic or specific problem to be considered is presented. A program capable of solving the problem, etc. is then given, together with examples of the output, sometimes for several different sets of conditions. Finally, in a section headed Program Notes the way the program is constructed and operates is comprehensively, yet concisely, explained and the engineering lessons to be learnt from the program output are indicated. Each chapter concludes with a set of problems for the student to attempt. These may involve some modification to programs presented in the examples, the development of a new general program which may be used to solve a whole class of problems or the construction of a program to solve a specific problem. Quite often even such a program could be modified to solve similar problems. It should be noted that, on occasion, the opportunity has been taken to include a new aspect of the basic theory in a problem over and above that included in the text.

The chapter topics are those which form the basis of a fundamental appreciation of civil engineering hydraulics commencing with a chapter that introduces the elements of fluid mechanics that may be considered, by and large, the starting points for the study of many different branches of fluid mechanics. Chapter 3 deals with flow in bounded systems – pipes and conduits – and includes not only the theory of steady flow but also an introduction to the theory of pressure transients in pipelines. In Chapter 4, open channel flow is introduced and includes uniform, rapidly varying and gradually varying flow, together with an introduction to unsteady channel flows. Chapter 5 introduces the theory of hydraulic machines laying particular emphasis on those machines that are of prime concern in civil engineering applications, with special reference to how such machines are matched to different operational requirements. The final chapter is concerned with groundwater and seepage flow, introducing the concept of potential functions to describe the flow associated with many different physical situations.

The author wishes to acknowledge the assistance and encouragement afforded by his colleague Dr M J Iremonger (Principal Lecturer in the Civil Engineering Department at RMCS) without which this book would not have been written. Thanks must also go to Professor W G Wood (Head of Materials Branch in the Civil Engineering Department at RMCS) who has enthusiastically promoted the use of BASIC computing in conjunction with engineering studies in the degree course and to the Civil Engineering Degree Course students at the College who have tried out (usually willingly) a number of the examples presented.

Finally, thanks are due to Mrs E Day for her expert manuscript preparation.

P.D.S.

Contents

Chapter 1

Introduction to BASIC

1.1 The BASIC approach

The programs in this book are written in the BASIC programming language. BASIC (Beginners All-purpose Symbolic Instruction Code) was developed at Dartmouth College, USA as an easy-to-learn general-purpose programming language. It was originally intended for use on time-sharing computer systems, but it has gained widespread popularity as the main language associated with microcomputers. The language is not only easy to learn but is also particularly easy to use. It is very simple to write a program, type it into the computer, run it and correct any errors and then run it again to obtain the required output in a quite short time.

The main disadvantages of simple BASIC relate to its lack of structure (see Section 1.4) but this is not an important consideration for short programs such as those presented in the following chapters.

This book is not an instruction manual on BASIC. If such a book is required the reader is referred to the works in the bibliography at the end of this chapter or to one of the many similar works. This book does aim, however, to help in the learning of BASIC by applying it to a relevant engineering subject. This aim can be met by the reader studying the examples and perhaps copying them and running them with different data and inputs and then trying some of the problems.

Although not a BASIC manual, a short description of the grammar of simple BASIC is given below so that the reader may be able to clarify any language problem rapidly.

1.2 The elements of BASIC

1.2.1 Mathematical expressions

One of the main objects of the example programs in this book is to evaluate and operate on the equations that arise in hydraulics. These equations contain numerical constants and variables (e.g. x) and functions (e.g. sin). All numbers are treated identically whether they be integers (e.g. 36) or real (e.g. 36.1). An exponential form is used to

1

represent large or small numbers (e.g. 3.61E6 represents 3.61×10^6). Numeric variables are represented by a letter or a letter followed by a digit (e.g. E or E1). On many computers π is directly available to the user either as PI or as a π key. (In this book PI has been used.) An operation such as a square root can be done by using an in-built function (e.g. SQR(X)). The argument in brackets (X) can be a number, a variable or a mathematical expression. For trigonometrical functions (SIN(X), COS(X), etc.) the argument is interpreted as being in radians. Other functions include a natural logarithm and its exponential (LOG and EXP respectively), ABS which selects the absolute value of the argument and INT which selects the integer part of the argument.

Mathematical equations also contain operators such as plus, minus, etc. These operators have a hierarchy in that some are performed by the computer before others. In descending order of hierarchy the operators are

to the power of $(\wedge)$
multiply (*) and divide (/)
add (+) and subtract (−).

Thus, for example, any multiplication is carried out before any addition. The computer works from left to right in an expression if the operators have the same hierarchy. The use of brackets allows any of these operations to be overridden. Hence $\dfrac{a + b}{3c}$ becomes (A + B)/(3*C) or (A + B)/B/C.

1.2.2 Program structure and assignment

A BASIC program is a sequence of statements which define a procedure for the computer to follow. As it follows this procedure, the computer allocates values to each of the variables. The values of some of these variables may be specified by data that are input to the program. Others are generated in the program using, for instance, the assignment statement. This has the form

line number [LET] variable = mathematical expression

where the word LET is usually optional and therefore omitted.

As an example, the root of a quadratic equation

$$x_1 = \frac{-b + \sqrt{b^2 - 4ac}}{2a}$$

may be obtained from a statement such as

$$100 \; X1 = (-B + SQR(B^2 - 4*A*C))/(2*A)$$

It is important to realise that an assignment statement is not itself an equation. Rather, it is an instruction to the computer to give the variable on the left-hand side the numeric value of the expression on the right-hand side. It is therefore possible to have a statement

$$50 \; X = X + 1$$

which increases by 1 the value of X. Each variable can have only one value at any time unless it is subscripted (see Section 1.2.7)

Note that all BASIC statements (i.e. all the program lines) are numbered. The line number defines the order in which such statements are executed.

1.2.3 Input

For interactive or 'conversational' programs the user specifies variables by inputting data in response to prompts from the computer as the program is running. The statement has the form

line number INPUT variable 1 [, variable 2, ...]

e.g.

20 INPUT A, B, C

When the program is run the computer prints ? as it reaches this statement and waits for the user to type values for the variables, e.g.

? 5, 10, 15

which makes A = 5, B = 10 and C = 15 in the example above.

An alternative form of data input is useful if there are many data or if the data are not to be changed by the user (e.g. a range of Reynolds numbers). For this type of data specification there is a statement of the form

line number READ variable 1 [, variable 2, ...]

e.g.

20 READ A, B, C

with an associated statement (or number of statements) of the form

line number DATA number 1 [, number 2, ...]

e.g.

1 DATA 5, 10, 15

or

1 DATA 5

2 DATA 10

3 DATA 15

DATA statements can be placed anywhere in a program – it is often convenient to place them at the beginning of the program so that they can be easily changed.

When using built-in data it is sometimes necessary to read data from their start more than once during a single program run. This is done using the statement

line number RESTORE

(though it has not be used in this book).

1.2.4 Output

Output of data and the results of calculations, etc. is implemented by using a statement of the form

Line number PRINT list

where the list may contain variables or expressions, e.g.

200 PRINT A, B, C, A*B/C

text enclosed in quotes, e.g.

10 PRINT "INPUT A, B, C IN MM"

or mixed text and variables, e.g.

300 PRINT "PRESSURE IS"; P; "N/MM^2"

The items in the list are separated by commas or semi-colons. Commas give tabulations in columns, each about 15 spaces wide, while a semi-colon suppresses this spacing. If a semi-colon is placed at the end of a list it has the function of suppressing the line feed. If the list is left empty a blank line is printed.

The necessity of using PRINT statements in association with both 'run-time' input (to indicate what input is required) and READ/DATA statements (because otherwise the program user has no record of the data) should be noted.

1.2.5 Conditional statements

It is often necessary to enable a program to take some action if, and only if, some condition is fulfilled. This is done with a statement of the form

> line number IF expression 1 conditional operator expression 2 THEN line number

where the possible conditional operators are

$= $ equals
$< >$ not equal to
$<$ less than
$< =$ less than or equal to
$>$ greater than
$> =$ greater than or equal to.

For example, a program could contain the following statements if it is to stop when a zero value of A is input

```
20 INPUT A
30 IF A <> 0 THEN 50
40 STOP
50 . . .
```

In this example, note the statement

> line number STOP

which stops the run of a program. The statement

> line number END

may be used at the end of a program though this is not essential.

1.2.6 Loops

There are several means by which a program can repeat some of its procedure. The simplest such statement is

> line number GO TO line number

This statement could be used with the conditional statement example above so that the program continues to request values of A until the user inputs zero.

The most common way of performing loops is with a starting statement of the form

> line number FOR variable = expression 1 TO expression 2 [STEP expression 3]

where the step is assumed to be unity if omitted. The finish of the loop is signified by a statement

> line number NEXT variable

where the same variable is used in both FOR and NEXT statements. Its value should not be changed in the intervening lines.

A loop is used if, for example, N sets of data have to be READ and their reciprocals printed, e.g.

```
10 READ N
20 PRINT "NUMBER", "RECIPROCAL"
30 FOR I = 1 TO N
40 READ A
50 PRINT A, 1/A
60 NEXT I
```

Loops can also be used to generate data. Consider the example given below of a simple temperature conversion program:

```
10 PRINT "CENTIGRADE", "FAHRENHEIT"
20 FOR C = 0 to 100 STEP 5
30 PRINT C, 9*C/5 + 32
40 NEXT C
```

1.2.7 Subscripted variables

It is sometimes very convenient to allow a single variable to have a number of different values during a single program run. For instance, if a program contains data for several different flow rates in a pipe it is convenient for these to be called $Q(1)$, $Q(2)$, $Q(3)$, etc. instead of $Q1$, $Q2$, $Q3$, etc. It is then possible for a single statement to perform calculations for all the flow rates e.g.

```
50 FOR I = 1 TO N
60 V(I) = Q(I)/A
70 NEXT I
```

which determines the velocity of flow in the pipe (which is of cross-sectional area A) for each flow-rate.

A non-subscripted variable has a single value associated with it and if a subscripted variable is used it is necessary to provide space for all the values. This is done with a dimensioning statement of the form

> line number DIM variable 1 (integer 1) [, variable 2 (integer 2),
> . . . . .]

e.g.

20 DIM V(20), Q(20)

which allows up to 20 values of V and Q. The DIM statement must occur before the subscripted variables are first used.

On some computers it is possible to use a dimension statement of a different form, e.g.

20 DIM V(N), Q(N)

where the value of N has been previously defined. This form, when available, has the advantage of not wasting storage space.

1.2.8 Subroutines

Sometimes a sequence of statements needs to be accessed more than once in the same program. Instead of merely repeating these statements it is better to put them in a subroutine. The program then contains statements of the form

line number GOSUB line number

When the program reaches this statement it branches (i.e. transfers control) to the second line number. The sequence of statements starting with this second line number ends with a statement

line number RETURN

and the program returns control to the statement immediately after the GOSUB call.

Subroutines can be placed anywhere in the program but it is usually convenient to position them at the end, separate from the main program statements.

Another reason for using a subroutine occurs when a procedure is written which is required in more than one program. In subroutines it is sometimes desirable to use less common variable names (e.g. X9 instead of X) so that the possibility of the same variable name being used with a different meaning in separate parts of the program is minimised.

1.2.9 Other statements

(1) Explanatory remarks or headings which are not to be output can be inserted into a program using

line number REM comment

Any statement beginning with the word REM is ignored by the computer. On some computers it is possible to include remarks on the same line as other statements.

(2) Non-numeric data (e.g. words) can be handled by string variables. A string is a series of characters within quotes (e.g. "PRESSURE") and a string variable is a letter followed by a $ sign (e.g. A$). String variables are particularly valuable when printed headings need to be changed.

(3) Multiple branching can be done with statements of the form

> line number ON expression THEN line number 1 [, line number 2, ...]

and

> line number ON expression GOSUB line number 1 [, line number 2, ...]

When a program reaches one of these statements it branches to line number 1 if the integer value of the expression is 1, to line number 2 if the expression is 2 and so on. An error message is printed if the expression gives a value less than 1 or greater than the number of referenced line numbers.

(4) Functions other than those built into the language such as SIN(X), etc. can be created by using a DEF statement. For example

> 10 DEF FNA(X) = X^3 + X^2

defines a cubic function which can be recalled later in the program as FNA (variable) where the value of this variable is substituted for X. A defined function is of use where an algebraic expression is to be evaluated several times in a program. (These last two statement forms have not been used in this book.)

1.3   Checking programs

Most computers give a clear indication if there are grammatical (syntax) errors in a BASIC program. Program statements can be modified by retyping them completely or by using special editing procedures. The majority of syntax errors are easy to locate but if a variable has been used with two (or more) different meanings in separate parts of the program some 'mystifying' errors can result.

It is not sufficient for the program to be just grammatically correct — it must also give the correct answers. A program should therefore be checked either by using data which give a known solution or by hand calculation.

If the program is to be used with a wide range of data or by users other than the program writer, it is necessary to check that all parts of it function. It is also important to ensure that the program does not give incorrect yet plausible answers when 'nonsense' data are input. It is quite difficult to make programs completely 'userproof' and they become somewhat lengthy by so doing. The programs in this book have been kept as short as possible for the purpose of clarity and may not therefore be fully 'userproof'.

1.4   Different computers and variants of BASIC

The examples in this book use a simple version of BASIC that should work on most computers, even those with small storage capacity. Only single line statements have been used though many computers allow a number of statements on each line with a separator such as /. Multiple assignments may also be possible so that, for instance, in Example 2.3 some simplification could be achieved by replacing lines 1000 to 1030 by a single statement such as

$$1000 \; A(0) = B(0) = C(0) = D(0) = 0$$

There is one important feature which distinguishes computers, particularly microcomputers with visual display units (VDU). This concerns the number of columns available across each line and the number of lines that are visible on the screen. Simple modifications to some of the example programs may be necessary to fit the output to a particular microcomputer. TAB printing is a useful facility for this purpose.

Various enhancements of BASIC have been made since its inception – these have been implemented on a number of computer systems. The programs in this book could be rewritten to take account of some of these 'advanced' features. For example, the ability to use long variable names (e.g. VELOCITY instead of say V or V1) makes it easier to write unambiguous programs. Other advanced facilities include more powerful looping and conditional statements and independent subroutines which make structured programs easier to write. Expressed simply, structured programming involves the compartmentalisation of programs and minimises branching resulting from statements containing 'GOTO line number' and 'THEN line number'. Good program structure is advantageous in long programs.

1.5   Summary of BASIC statements

Assignment
LET   Computes and assigns value
DIM   Allows space for subscripted variables

Input
INPUT   Reads data from 'run-time' keyboard input

READ	Reads data from DATA statements
DATA	Storage area for data
RESTORE	Restores data to its start

Output

PRINT	Prints output list

Program control

STOP	Stops program
IF. . . THEN	Conditional branching
GO TO	Unconditional branching
FOR. . .TO. . .STEP	Opens loop
NEXT	Closes loop
GOSUB	Transfers control to subroutine
RETURN	Return from subroutine
ON. . .THEN	Multiple branching
ON. . .GOSUB	Multiple subroutine transfer
END	Last line of program

Comment

REM	Comment in program

Functions

SQR	Square root
SIN	Sine (angle in radians)
COS	Cosine (angle in radians)
ATN	Arctangent (gives angle in radians)
LOG	Natural logarithm (base e)
EXP	Exponential
ABS	Absolute value
INT	Integer value
DEF FN	Defined function

1.6 Bibliography

The books noted below represent only a fraction of those available on BASIC programming.

1. Alcock, D., *Illustrating BASIC,* Cambridge University Press, (1977).
2. Forsyth, R., *The BASIC Idea,* Chapman and Hall, (1978).
3. Gottfried, B.S., *Programming with BASIC —Schaum's Outline Series,* McGraw-Hill, (1975).
4. Kemeny, J.G. and Kurtz, T.E., *BASIC Programming,* Wiley, (1968).
5. Monro, D.M., *Interactive Computing with BASIC,* Arnold, (1974).

Chapter 2

Elements of fluid mechanics

ESSENTIAL THEORY

2.1 Introduction

Matter can exist as a solid in which intermolecular bonds are strong and applied compressive, tensile and shear forces produce finite deformations, or as a liquid in which intermolecular bonding is weaker and, while compressive forces are resisted, shear forces can cause deformation indefinitely, or finally as a gas in which bonds are very weak and any applied force produces shape and volume changes. Liquids and gases are fluids and, despite their molecular structure, are assumed to be continuous at normal pressures and densities, etc.

A fluid may therefore be defined as matter which will deform continually and without limit under the action of an external resultant force, however small. In this book the principal working fluid will be water.

2.2 Properties of fluids

In the table below the principal parameters that define a fluid are summarised.

	Symbol	SI unit	Comment
Density	ρ	kg/m³	mass per unit volume
Specific weight	W	N/m³	weight per unit volume
Specific gravity	S	–	ratio of densities of fluid and water
Pressure	p	Pascals or N/m² or m or bar	acts normally to surface of body
Dynamic viscosity	μ	kg/ms	a measure of the internal friction of a fluid
Kinematic viscosity	ν	m²/s	μ/ρ
Bulk modulus	K	N/m²	a measure of resistance of a fluid to compression forces
Speed of sound	c	m/s	speed of a pressure wave through a fluid

11

2.3 Hydrostatics

By considering the equilibrium of a small element of fluid at rest in a large volume the change in pressure dp downward through the fluid through a distance dz is given by

$$\frac{dp}{dz} = -\rho g \qquad (2.1)$$

Integration of this equation for a fluid with a free surface as shown in Figure 2.1 gives the pressure at A at a depth h below the surface as

$$p = p_a + \rho g h \qquad (2.2)$$

where p_a is atmospheric pressure. It is often convenient to express pressures relative to atmospheric pressure as gauge pressures. Thus, the gauge static pressure at A is

$$p_g = \rho g h \qquad (2.3)$$

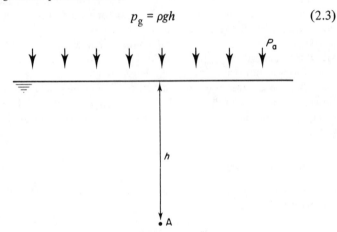

Figure 2.1 Pressure variation with depth below free surface

2.4   Measurement of static pressure

Measurement of static pressure is often accomplished by means of a manometer in which a column of fluid is balanced against the unknown pressure. For the simple U-tube manometer shown in Figure 2.2 the pressure p in the vessel attached to arm A of the manometer is given by

$$p = p_a + \rho_m g h \qquad (2.4)$$

or as a gauge pressure p_g by

$$p_g = \rho_m g h \qquad (2.5)$$

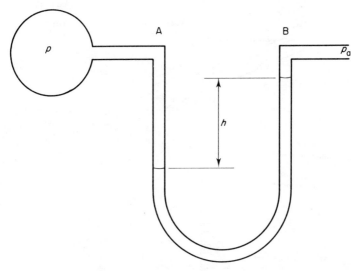

Figure 2.2 Simple U-tube manometer

where ρ_m is the density of fluid in the manometer. For greater measuring accuracy the manometer tube may be inclined and a large reservoir attached to one limb thus allowing a greater movement to be measured (Figure 2.3(a)) or the manometer may contain two immiscible fluids with different but similar densities (Figure 2.3(b)) in which the pressure applied to arm A is given by

$$p = (\rho_2 - \rho_1)gh \qquad (2.6)$$

where ρ_1 and ρ_2 are the densities of fluids in A and B respectively.

2.5   Forces on plane and curved surfaces

The resultant force acting on the flat plate shown in Figure 2.4 is given by

$$R = \rho g A \bar{y} \qquad (2.7)$$

where the plate is of area A with its centroid G at a depth $\bar{y}$ below the free surface of the fluid. The resultant force acts at C a depth D below the free surface where

$$D = (\sin^2 \phi K_G{}^2 / \bar{y}) + \bar{y} \qquad (2.8)$$

ϕ is the angle of inclination of the plate to the free surface and K_G is the radius of gyration of the plate about its centroid.

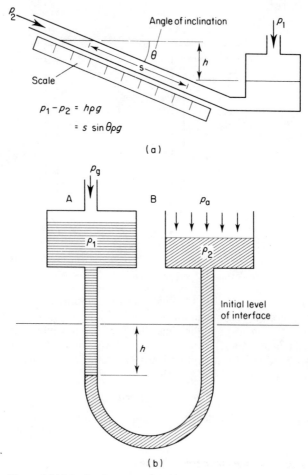

Figure 2.3(a) Inclined tube manometer (*b*) Two-fluid manometer

For the curved plate AB shown in Figure 2.5 the resultant force R has a horizontal component R_h (which is the hydrostatic force acting over the projection of AB in the vertical plane, AC, and acts at the centre of pressure F) and a vertical component R_v (which is entirely due to the weight of the fluid above the plate in the volume represented by ABDE and acts through the centre of gravity of ABED at G). The resultant acts through O at an angle θ given by

$$\tan\theta = R_v/R_h \qquad (2.9)$$

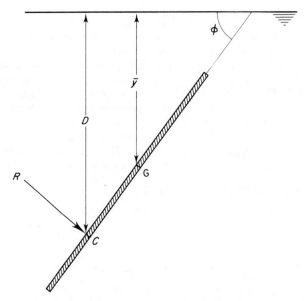

Figure 2.4 Submerged flat plate [after Douglas, Gasiorek, Swaffield, *Fluid Mechanics,* Pitman, (1979)]

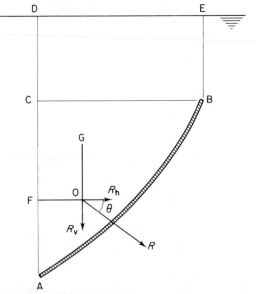

Figure 2.5 Forces on submerged curved plate [after Douglas, Gasiorek, Swaffield, *Fluid Mechanics,* Pitman, (1979)]

2.6   Buoyancy and floating stability

Archimedes' principle states that the upthrust experienced by a body in a fluid is equal to the weight of fluid displaced.

In the design of floating structures (e.g. bridge pontoons, oil-rigs, ships, navigation buoys, etc.) it is important that a stable configuration is achieved. The completely submerged body shown in Figure 2.6(a) will, if disturbed from its equilibrium position, right itself because the couple caused by the weight of the body acting through the centre of gravity G and the upthrust acting through the centre of buoyancy B is a restoring (anticlockwise) moment. The body shown in Figure 2.6(b), however, will overturn if disturbed because the couple is clockwise.

A similar approach may be applied to a partially submerged body as illustrated in Figure 2.7, where a floating bridge pontoon is shown in a

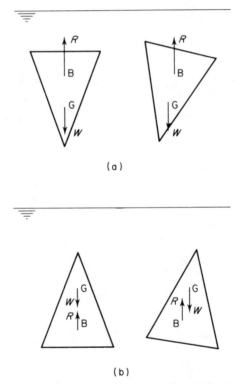

(a)

(b)

Figure 2.6(a) Completely submerged stable body (*b*) Completely submerged unstable body [after Douglas, Gasiorek, Swaffield, *Fluid Mechanics,* Pitman, (1979)]

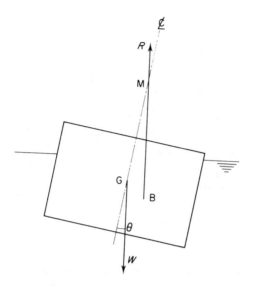

Figure 2.7 Partially submerged floating body

disturbed position tilted at an angle θ. The couple will restore equilibrium provided that the point M, known as the metacentre, located
where the line of action of the buoyancy force cuts the original centre
line of the body, is above the centre of gravity G. For small angles of
tilt, the restoring couple C is

$$C = Wm\theta \qquad (2.10)$$

where W is the weight of the body and m, the distance between G and
M, is the metacentric height.

   Metacentric height may be determined experimentally by considering
two equilibrium positions of a body when a small weight P is moved
across the top of a floating structure as shown in Figure 2.8(a) and (b).
The second equilibrium position (Figure 2.8(b)) is with the weight
shifted a distance x and the structure tilted by θ. The metacentric
height (which is found to be nearly constant whatever values of x and
θ are measured) is

$$m = Px/W\theta \qquad (2.11)$$

Analytically, it may be shown that the metacentric height is related to
the distance (b) between the original (undisturbed) position of the
centre of buoyancy B and the centre of gravity of the body G, I, the
second moment of area of the plane of the body cut by the waterline

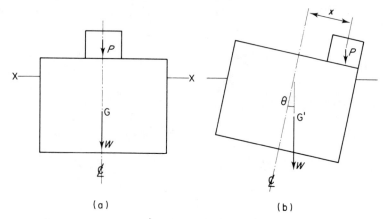

Figure 2.8(a) Floating body: equilibrium position 1 (*b*) Floating
body: equilibrium position 2

(XX in Figure 2.8(a)) and the volume of fluid displaced, V, by the
equation

$$m = (I/V) - b \tag{2.12}$$

2.7 Basic fluid dynamics

In this section the basic concepts of fluid motion will be introduced.
  Elements of a flowing fluid may move with different velocities and
undergo different accelerations but each element must conform to the
basic principles of mechanics. The concept that mass can be neither
created nor destroyed leads to the equation of continuity. Any change
in velocity causing an acceleration requires a force to produce the
change. This idea leads to the force/momentum equation. Finally, the
concept that energy cannot be created or destroyed (only converted
from one form to another) leads to the formulation of the energy
equation. Before the forms of these equations are written, several
points about the kinetics of fluid flow should be made.
  Steady flow is flow in which fluid parameters are constant with
respect to time. Thus, for example

$$\frac{\partial v}{\partial t} = \frac{\partial p}{\partial t} = \frac{\partial \rho}{\partial t} = 0 \tag{2.13}$$

In unsteady flow

$$\frac{\partial v}{\partial t} \neq 0 \quad \text{etc.} \tag{2.14}$$

Uniform flow is that flow in which the velocity vector is identical everywhere in the flow. For example

$$\frac{\partial u}{\partial x} = \frac{\partial v}{\partial x} = \frac{\partial v}{\partial y} = \frac{\partial w}{\partial z} = 0 \qquad (2.15)$$

where u, v, w are the components of the velocity vector. In non-uniform flow, conditions do vary from point to point.

The paths of fluid particles in a flow may usefully be described by the following terms:

(1) *streamline:* velocity at any point is in the direction of the tangent to the line at that point. There is no flow across a streamline;
(2) *streamtube:* a tube in the flow whose surface is composed of streamlines. There is no flow across the surface and the velocity is constant across a section (see Figure 2.9);

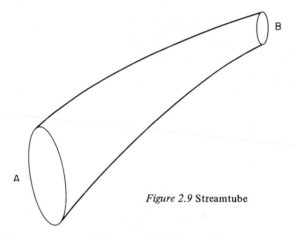

Figure 2.9 Streamtube

(3) *pathline:* the line traced out by an individual particle in the fluid;
(4) *streakline:* the line traced out by a succession of particles which have all passed through a particular fixed point.

In steady flow, streamlines, streaklines and pathlines are coincident but this may not be the case in unsteady flow.

2.8 Continuity equation

For the streamtube shown in Figure 2.9 the velocity, cross-sectional area and fluid density at A are U_A, A_A and ρ_A while at end B they are U_B, A_B and ρ_B. The principle of conservation of mass requires that

$$\dot{m} = \rho_A \, U_A \, A_A = \rho_B \, U_B \, A_B \qquad (2.16)$$

where $\dot{m}$ is the mass flow rate of fluid.

With incompressible flow as in, for example, water where density is constant, the volumetric flow rate Q is given by

$$Q = UA = \text{const.} \qquad (2.17)$$

2.9 Energy equation

If the streamtube shown in Figure 2.9 is considered to be elemental, with pressure, cross-sectional area, velocity of fluid and density at end A equal to p, A, u and ρ respectively, and at end B equal to p + dp, A + dA, u + du and ρ + dρ then, if the streamtube is of length ds and is at height z above some datum level Euler's energy equation for steady, one-dimensional, inviscid flow is given by

$$\frac{1}{\rho}\frac{dp}{ds} + g\frac{dz}{ds} + u\frac{du}{ds} = 0 \qquad (2.18)$$

and describes the changes in flow conditions along a thin streamtube which, in the limit, may be considered as a streamline. If the fluid is incompressible (ρ constant) then Euler's equation may be integrated to give

$$\frac{p}{\rho} + gz + \tfrac{1}{2}u^2 = \text{const. along streamline} \qquad (2.19)$$

This is Bernoulli's equation which may be rearranged as

$$p + \rho gz + \tfrac{1}{2}\rho u^2 = \text{const.} \qquad (2.20)$$

in which the first term is static pressure, the second may be considered as a gravity term (where z is measured from any convenient horizontal datum plane) and the third term is called the dynamic pressure. The constant is sometimes termed total pressure. When referring to a liquid it is convenient to divide Equation (2.20) through by ρg and rewrite it to give

$$h + z + \tfrac{1}{2}u^2/g = H \qquad (2.21)$$

where all the terms have the dimensions of length; h is the static head in metres and H is total head. Bernoulli's equation finds wide application in, for instance, the measurement of fluid velocity by means of a pitot tube attached to an aircraft or measurement of discharge in a pipe by means of a venturi meter, orifice plate or flow nozzle.

2.10 Momentum equation

It is important to define the direction in which the momentum equation is to be applied since forces are vectors. For convenience, components of force or momentum will be considered in the x-direction only. Similar equations will apply to any other direction. The momentum equation states that the sum of the forces acting on a volume of fluid equals the rate of change of momentum of the fluid. Thus, referring to the streamtube of Figure 2.9, if the velocity at end A is U_A and at end B it is U_B and the volume flow rate through the streamtube is Q, then the sum of forces in the x-direction is given by

$$F_x = \rho Q [(U_x)_B - (U_x)_A] \qquad (2.22)$$

where $(U_x)_A$ and $(U_x)_B$ are the components of velocity in the x-direction at A and B respectively. The momentum equation finds many applications in hydraulics, generally employed in conjunction with the continuity and Bernoulli equations. Examples include the analysis of a hydraulic jump in a channel, the evaluation of the force exerted by a water jet on a vane of a hydraulic machine and the calculation of the force exerted on a pipe-bend in a pipe-network.

2.11 Fluid viscosity

In many cases exact mathematical description of fluid flow is not possible and it is necessary to rely on experimental results to furnish a description of real flows.

For example, Bernoulli's equation is valid only for inviscid fluids and total pressure will actually decrease along a streamline because of the work needed to overcome viscous forces (which are particularly important where fluid is in contact with a fixed boundary).

Reynolds was the first to realise the full significance of viscosity in real flow when he conducted his famous dye trace experiments in a pipe. He was able to identify laminar flow in which the dye trace was essentially undisturbed (and in which fluid viscosity is the dominant factor) and turbulent flow where the dye was dispersed across the cross-section of the pipe (and in which fluid inertial forces dominate). By combining the parameters that were varied in the experiments, Reynolds obtained a non-dimensional number (named in his honour), the Reynolds number, Re, where

$$\text{Re} = \rho U d / \mu \qquad (2.23)$$

where ρ is fluid density, d is pipe diameter, U is mean fluid velocity and μ is dynamic viscosity. At low values of Re (<2000) flow was laminar and at Re >4000 flow was seen to be turbulent. Between these two extremes an intermediate phase termed transition flow was observed. Extension of the results for pipe flow to other flows (such as flows past solid bodies) in which viscosity is significant, leads to the conclusion that the nature of the flow is Reynolds number dependent and further that Reynolds number may be considered to be the ratio of inertia forces to viscous forces and that streamline patterns will be determined by the value of Re and the body shape.

Depending on the value of flow Reynolds number (based on mean fluid velocity and a characteristic dimension of the body) the flow near the body surface will have very definite characteristics. The velocity of the fluid in contact with the surface will be zero and this will increase to the free stream velocity in a very short distance in what is known as the boundary layer. Typical velocity profiles for laminar and turbulent boundary layers are shown in Figure 2.10 for the development of the boundary layer over a flat plate in which the characteristic length used in the Reynolds number will be the distance x from the leading edge of the plate.

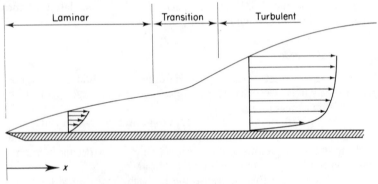

Figure 2.10 Development of a boundary layer along a flat plate

For a boundary layer growing on a body the nature of the layer will determine the ease with which the layer may be separated from the body surface under the action of an adverse pressure gradient. A laminar layer will separate more easily than a turbulent layer so for flow over a circular cylinder, shown in Figure 2.11(a) and (b), the laminar layer separates at about $90°$ causing a wide wake (in which there is considerable momentum loss) and hence a high drag while the turbulent layer separates later (at about $120°$) causing lower overall drag. Thus the inhibition of boundary layer separation leads to low drag forces as required in, for example, an aerofoil.

It is usual to relate drag force (non-dimensionalised as a drag coefficient) to Reynolds number as illustrated by Example 2.4. Generally

Example 2.1 PRESCON: conversion of pressure units   23

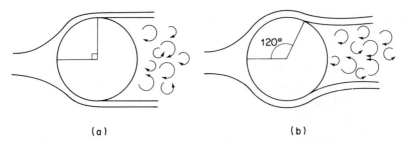

(a)   (b)

Figure 2.11(a) Low Re flow round circular cylinder *(b)* High Re
flow round circular cylinder

the use of non-dimensional numbers reduces the number of experiments
required to furnish a complete assessment of the behaviour of a fluid
system as illustrated by the examples of Chapters 3 and 5.

WORKED EXAMPLES

Example 2.1 PRESCON: conversion of pressure units

The pressure in a fluid can be expressed in many different units and
some confusion can arise as to the relationship of one form of notation
to another. In basic SI units pressure can be expressed in N/m^2 where
$1 N/m^2$ is known as a Pascal. It is often convenient to express large
pressures in terms of bars where 1 bar equals $10^5 N/m^2$. In order to
gain some subjective feel for the quantities involved in the design of,
say, a pressure vessel, pressures may be expressed in atmospheric units
where 1 atmosphere is 1.013 bar. Alternatively, a hydraulic engineer
concerned with the design of a reservoir store and water supply system
would express pressures in terms of the head of the working fluid as
metres of water. Multiplication of the head of fluid by fluid density and
gravitational acceleration g gives pressure in N/m^2 again.

Finally, although SI is now the accepted system, pressures are
still expressed in Imperial units as pounds per square inch (psi) where 1
psi equals $6895 N/m^2$.

The following program allows the conversion of a pressure input in
one of the units mentioned above to all the other units.

```
PRESCON     2-JUL-81   09:03:49

10 PRINT 'PROGRAM FOR CONVERSION OF PRESSURES'
20 PRINT
30 PRINT 'HOW IS PRESSURE DATA TO BE INPUT?'
40 PRINT 'AS HEAD OF FLUID? (OPTION A)'
50 PRINT 'AS ABSOLUTE PRESSURE IN N/M^2? (OPTION B)'
60 PRINT 'AS ABSOLUTE PRESSURE IN PSI? (OPTION C)'
70 PRINT 'AS ABSOLUTE PRESSURE IN BAR? (OPTION D)'
```

```
80 PRINT "AS NUMBER OF ATMOSPHERES? (OPTION E)"
90 INPUT A$
100 IF A$="A" GO TO 160
110 IF A$="B" GO TO 330
120 IF A$="C" GO TO 390
130 IF A$="D" GO TO 440
140 IF A$="E" GO TO 490
150 PRINT
160 PRINT "WHAT IS DENSITY OF FLUID USED TO GIVE HEAD (KG/M^3) ";
170 INPUT D
180 PRINT "WHAT IS VALUE OF HEAD IN METRES?";
190 INPUT H
200 PRINT
210 H1=H*D/1000
220 P1=H1*9.81*1000
230 P2=P1/6895
240 P3=P1/100000
250 P4=P1/(100000*1.013)
260 PRINT "HEAD","ABS P","ABS P","ABS P","ATMOS"
270 PRINT "M WATER","N/M^2","PSI","BAR"," "
280 PRINT "_____"
290 PRINT H1,P1,P2,P3,P4
300 PRINT
310 GO TO 530
320 PRINT
330 PRINT "WHAT IS ABSOLUTE PRESSURE IN N/M^2?";
340 INPUT P1
350 H1=P1/(1000*9.81)
360 PRINT
370 GO TO 230
380 PRINT
390 PRINT "WHAT IS ABSOLUTE PRESSURE IN PSI?";
400 INPUT P2
410 P1=P2*6895
420 GO TO 350
430 PRINT
440 PRINT "WHAT IS PRESSURE IN BAR?";
450 INPUT P3
460 P1=P3*100000
470 GO TO 350
480 PRINT
490 PRINT "WHAT IS PRESSURE IN ATMOSPHERES?";
500 INPUT P4
510 P1=P4*100000*1.013
520 GO TO 350
530 PRINT "ANY FURTHER DATA TO CONVERT? (Y/N)?";
540 INPUT B$
550 IF B$="Y" GO TO 30
560 END

READY



RUN


PRESCON    2-JUL-81  09:04:50

PROGRAM FOR CONVERSION OF PRESSURES

HOW IS PRESSURE DATA TO BE INPUT?
AS HEAD OF FLUID? (OPTION A)
AS ABSOLUTE PRESSURE IN N/M^2? (OPTION B)
AS ABSOLUTE PRESSURE IN PSI? (OPTION C)
AS ABSOLUTE PRESSURE IN BAR? (OPTION D)
AS NUMBER OF ATMOSPHERES? (OPTION E)
? A
WHAT IS DENSITY OF FLUID USED TO GIVE HEAD (KG/M^3)?? 784
WHAT IS VALUE OF HEAD IN METRES?? 0.25
```

Example 2.1 PRESCON: conversion of pressure units   25

```
HEAD        ABS P        ABS P        ABS P        ATMOS
M WATER     N/M^2        PSI          BAR
------------------------------------------------------------
.196        1922.76      .278863      .0192276     .0189809

ANY FURTHER DATA TO CONVERT? (Y/N)?? Y
HOW IS PRESSURE DATA TO BE INPUT?
AS HEAD OF FLUID? (OPTION A)
AS ABSOLUTE PRESSURE IN N/M^2? (OPTION B)
AS ABSOLUTE PRESSURE IN PSI? (OPTION C)
AS ABSOLUTE PRESSURE IN BAR? (OPTION D)
AS NUMBER OF ATMOSPHERES? (OPTION E)
? B
WHAT IS ABSOLUTE PRESSURE IN N/M^2?? 101300

HEAD        ABS P        ABS P        ABS P        ATMOS
M WATER     N/M^2        PSI          BAR
------------------------------------------------------------
10.3262     101300       14.6918      1.013        1

ANY FURTHER DATA TO CONVERT? (Y/N)?? Y
HOW IS PRESSURE DATA TO BE INPUT?
AS HEAD OF FLUID? (OPTION A)
AS ABSOLUTE PRESSURE IN N/M^2? (OPTION B)
AS ABSOLUTE PRESSURE IN PSI? (OPTION C)
AS ABSOLUTE PRESSURE IN BAR? (OPTION D)
AS NUMBER OF ATMOSPHERES? (OPTION E)
? C
WHAT IS ABSOLUTE PRESSURE IN PSI?? 14.7

HEAD        ABS P        ABS P        ABS P        ATMOS
M WATER     N/M^2        PSI          BAR
------------------------------------------------------------
10.332      101357       14.7         1.01357      1.00056

ANY FURTHER DATA TO CONVERT? (Y/N)?? Y

HOW IS PRESSURE DATA TO BE INPUT?
AS HEAD OF FLUID? (OPTION A)
AS ABSOLUTE PRESSURE IN N/M^2? (OPTION B)
AS ABSOLUTE PRESSURE IN PSI? (OPTION C)
AS ABSOLUTE PRESSURE IN BAR? (OPTION D)
AS NUMBER OF ATMOSPHERES? (OPTION E)
? D
WHAT IS PRESSURE IN BAR?? 1.013

HEAD        ABS P        ABS P        ABS P        ATMOS
M WATER     N/M^2        PSI          BAR
------------------------------------------------------------
10.3262     101300       14.6918      1.013        1

ANY FURTHER DATA TO CONVERT? (Y/N)?? Y
HOW IS PRESSURE DATA TO BE INPUT?
AS HEAD OF FLUID? (OPTION A)
AS ABSOLUTE PRESSURE IN N/M^2? (OPTION B)
AS ABSOLUTE PRESSURE IN PSI? (OPTION C)
AS ABSOLUTE PRESSURE IN BAR? (OPTION D)
AS NUMBER OF ATMOSPHERES? (OPTION E)
? E
WHAT IS PRESSURE IN ATMOSPHERES?? 7

HEAD        ABS P        ABS P        ABS P        ATMOS
M WATER     N/M^2        PSI          BAR
------------------------------------------------------------
72.2834     709100       102.843      7.091        7

ANY FURTHER DATA TO CONVERT? (Y/N)?? N

READY
```

Program notes

(1) In lines 30 to 90 the operator selects the units in which the pressure data are to be input by making the appropriate response to the prompts at lines 40, 50, 60, 70 and 80. Depending on the input at 90 the program will go to the required section as indicated in lines 100–140.

(2) If data are to be input as head of fluid in metres the operator inputs the particular fluid density at line 170 as D and the head of fluid at 190 as H. At line 210 this head is converted to metres of water (H1). At line 220 this head of water is converted to N/m^2 (P1) while at line 230 this pressure is converted to psi (P2). At lines 240 and 250 Pl is converted to bar (P3) and atmospheres (P4) respectively.

(3) With the relevant quantities evaluated, appropriate headings are printed at lines 260 and 270 before the results are output at line 290. The program then goes to line 530 to find out whether any further data are to be input, depending on the response to the prompt, i.e. the string variable B$.

(4) If pressure is to be input in N/m^2 the value is input as P1 at line 340 and converted to metres of water at line 350 (H1). Then by going to line 230 from 370 the program between lines 230 and 310 can be utilised.

(5) For pressure input as absolute values in psi (P2) at line 400 this is converted to N/m^2 (P1) at 410. The program returns to 350 for conversion of P1 to H1 before going to 230 as described in (4) above. A similar procedure is used to convert pressures input as bar or atmospheres at lines 450 and 500. In each case a printout of the appropriate pressure conversions is made as illustrated in the output format.

Example 2.2 SLUICEDES: design of radial sluice gate

A radial sluice gate consists of a cylindrical plate holding back a certain head of water in a river or man-made channel. Radial supports meet at the centre of the circle of which the arc is part where a bearing capable of resisting the thrust of the water is incorporated. Because the resultant pressure force on the cylindrical surface must act radially it passes through the centre of the circle O as illustrated in Figure 2.12. Thus, to control the flow under the sluice, achieved by raising and lowering the structure pivotted at O, only sufficient force to overcome the dead weight of the gate is required since there is no contribution from hydrostatic thrust when moments are taken about the pivot. It is required that a sluice gate be designed to retain a maximum head of 4 m of water. A variety of thrust bearings of different ratings are available and

Example 2.2 SLUICEDES: design of radial sluice gate   27

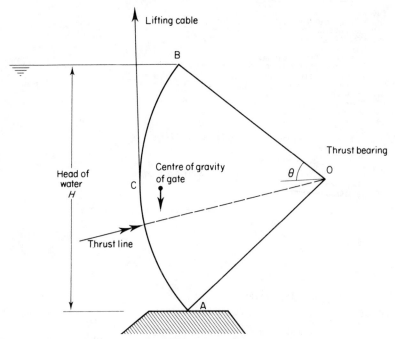

Figure 2.12 Radial sluice gate [after Douglas, Gasiorek, Swaffield, *Fluid Mechanics,* Pitman (1979)]

it is important that the structure does not extend too far in the downstream direction (thus introducing problems associated with the fixing of the bearing on the main sluice construction) and that the bearing is chosen with a factor of safety of approximately 2 such that any unexpected loadings on the sluice (i.e. impact by floating debris, boats, etc.) can be safely accommodated.

The following program allows the investigation of a number of different geometries and bearing capacities.

```
LIST

SLUICEDES  2-JUL-81  09:11:58

10 PRINT "DESIGN OF RADIAL SLUICE GATES"
20 PRINT
30 PRINT "MAXIMUM HEAD OF WATER TO IMPOUND  (M)=   ";
40 INPUT H
50 PRINT
60 PRINT "WIDTH OF SLUICE GATE (M)=";
70 INPUT W
80 PRINT
90 PRINT
100 PRINT "MAXIMUM THRUST THAT EACH BEARING CAN SUSTAIN (KN)=   ";
110 INPUT M
```

```
120 PRINT
130 PRINT "ANGLE","RADIUS","THRUST","SAFETY"
140 PRINT "(DEG)","M","KN","FACTOR"
150 FOR X=.1309 TO 1.5708 STEP .1309
160 R=(H/2)/SIN(X)
170 R1=.5*9.81*1000*H*H*W
180 R2=R*R*9.81*1000*(X-.5*SIN(2*X))*W
190 T1=SQR(R1^2+R2^2)/1000
200 T=T1/2
210 Y=X*180/PI
220 S=M/T
230 IF T>M GO TO 260
240 PRINT Y,R,T,S
250 GO TO 280
260 PRINT Y,R,T,"THRUST TOO LARGE"
270 GO TO 290
280 NEXT X
290 PRINT
300 PRINT "DO YOU WISH TO TRY WITH ANOTHER BEARING? (Y/N)";
310 INPUT A$
320 IF A$="Y" GO TO 80
330 END

READY



RUN

SLUICEDES  2-JUL-81  09:12:35

DESIGN OF RADIAL SLUICE GATES

MAXIMUM HEAD OF WATER TO IMPOUND  (M)=   ? 4

WIDTH OF SLUICE GATE (M)=? 2

MAXIMUM THRUST THAT EACH BEARING CAN SUSTAIN (KN)=   ? 80

ANGLE       RADIUS      THRUST      SAFETY
(DEG)       M           KN          FACTOR
 7.50002    15.3226     78.555      1.01839
15          7.72739     78.7838     1.01544
22.5001     5.22624     79.1778     1.01038
30.0001     3.99999     79.7576     1.00304
37.5001     3.28535     80.5544     THRUST TOO LARGE

DO YOU WISH TO TRY WITH ANOTHER BEARING? (Y/N)? Y


MAXIMUM THRUST THAT EACH BEARING CAN SUSTAIN (KN)=   ? 200

ANGLE       RADIUS      THRUST      SAFETY
(DEG)       M           KN          FACTOR
 7.50002    15.3226     78.555      2.54599
15          7.72739     78.7838     2.53859
22.5001     5.22624     79.1778     2.52596
30.0001     3.99999     79.7576     2.5076
37.5001     3.28535     80.5544     2.4828
45.0001     2.82842     81.6136     2.45057
52.5001     2.52094     82.9998     2.40964
60.0001     2.3094      84.804      2.35838
67.5002     2.16478     87.1551     2.29476
75.0002     2.07055     90.2375     2.21637
82.5002     2.01726     94.3185     2.12048

DO YOU WISH TO TRY WITH ANOTHER BEARING? (Y/N)? Y
```

Example 2.2 SLUICEDES: design of radial sluice gate   29

```
MAXIMUM THRUST THAT EACH BEARING CAN SUSTAIN (KN)=   ? 175

ANGLE          RADIUS          THRUST          SAFETY
(DEG)          M               KN              FACTOR
 7.50002        15.3226         78.555          2.22774
15              7.72739         78.7838         2.22127
22.5001          5.22624         79.1778         2.21021
30.0001          3.99999         79.7576         2.19415
37.5001          3.28535         80.5544         2.17245
45.0001          2.82842         81.6136         2.14425
52.5001          2.52094         82.9998         2.10844
60.0001          2.3094          84.804          2.06358
67.5002          2.16478         87.1551         2.00791
75.0002          2.07055         90.2375         1.93933
82.5002          2.01726         94.3185         1.85542

DO YOU WISH TO TRY WITH ANOTHER BEARING? (Y/N)?  N
```

Program notes

(1) In response to the prompt at line 30, the maximum head of water that requires to be impounded is input as H. The total sluice width is input as W at 70. At line 100 the operator is asked to select a bearing of particular thrust rating which is input as M at line 110.

(2) The important parameters that require evaluation are the angle subtended by the sluice gate (here the half angle θ in Figure 2.12 is used), the radius of the sluice gate, the thrust that the gate must sustain and the safety factor based on the bearing capacity. These headings are printed at lines 130 and 140 before calculation commences.

(3) The main calculation is executed in the loop between the lines 150 to 280. The variable X, the half angle subtended by the sluice, is stepped in $7.5°$ steps from $7.5°$ to $82.5°$ (i.e. 0.1309 radians to 1.5708 radians in 0.1309 radian steps). Using the current value of X the radius of the gate based on the maximum head of water H is found as R. At line 170 the total horizontal thrust component R1 is found. This is simply the hydrostatic pressure force given by $\frac{1}{2}\rho g H^2 W$. The upthrust on the sluice gate R2 is found from Archimedes' principle and is essentially the weight of fluid that has been displaced from the sector ABC in Figure 2.12. At line 190 the resultant thrust T1 is evaluated and in the subsequent line the thrust on each of the two bearings that will be required at each end of the sluice is evaluated as T. At line 210 the angle X is converted to Y degrees and the safety factor S is calculated at line 220. If the thrust exceeds the bearing capacity the program goes to line 260 and indicates this excess thrust by printing 'THRUST TOO LARGE' before asking for a new bearing capacity to be input. If S is greater than unity the parameters Y, R, T and S are printed before the next X value is taken. Further bearing capacities can be input if required.

(4) From the results it is seen that the selection of a bearing of 80 kN capacity would suffice but the safety factor is only just greater than

unity. The use of a bearing of capacity 200 kN meets the safety requirements over the whole range but, for a gate of fairly acute angle (i.e.
about 30° half angle), the safety factor is exceeded by over 25%. For
this reason a bearing of capacity 175 kN would be selected and the
sluice gate would have a radius of 4 m and thus subtend a total angle
of 60°.

Example 2.3 METACENT: stability of floating body

A toy company wishes to market a bath-time toy which will float, tilt
and roll while still remaining stable. The toy consists of a base into
which fits a vertical mast and two movable weights, one of weight 0.2 N
which locates in various places on the deck and the other which can be
fixed anywhere on the mast. The complete toy weighs 2.5 N and is

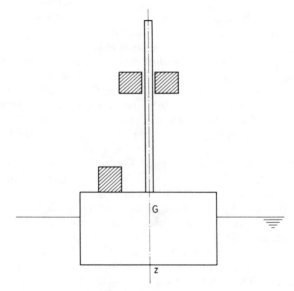

Figure 2.13 Floating bath-time toy

shown in Figure 2.13. Three experiments conducted on the toy are
reported below. The angles of tilt of the toy with different deck weight
locations for different mast weight positions are given together with the
distance between the centre of gravity G and the bottom of the base Z.
In each case the metacentric height must be evaluated and an estimate
made of the maximum possible value of GZ such that the toy always
remains stable, thus enabling the company to determine a suitable mast
height. The experimental data are as follows

Example 2.3 METACENT: stability of floating body   31

Position of deck weight from centreline (mm)	Angle of tilt (degrees)		
	Expt 1	Expt 2	Expt 3
5	0.9	0.5	0.3
20	3.6	2.1	1.4
35	6.4	3.9	2.7
50	8.6	5.4	3.8
GZ (mm)	91	75	58

```
LIST


METACENT    2-JUL-81   09:19:23

1 DATA 5,20,35,50
2 DATA 0.9,3.6,6.4,8.6
3 DATA 0.5,2.1,3.9,5.4
4 DATA 0.3,1.4,2.7,3.8
5 DATA 91,75,58
10 PRINT "ESTIMATION OF METACENTRIC HT AND LIMIT OF C OF G"
20 PRINT
30 PRINT "TOTAL WEIGHT OF VESSEL (N)=  ";
40 INPUT W1
50 PRINT "MOVEABLE WEIGHT (N)=  ";
60 INPUT W2
70 PRINT "HOW MANY EXPERIMENTS?  ";
80 INPUT M
90 PRINT "HOW MANY PAIRS OF DATA POINTS PER EXPT?  ";
100 INPUT N
110 FOR I=1 TO N
120 READ X(I)
130 NEXT I
140 FOR I=1 TO M
150 FOR J=1 TO N
160 READ Y(J)
170 NEXT J
180 GOSUB 1000
190 S(I)=(N*A(N)-B(N)*C(N))/(N*D(N)-B(N)*B(N))
200 G(I)=(W2/W1)*(180/PI)/S(I)
210 NEXT I
220 FOR I=1 TO M
230 READ Y(I)
240 X(I)=G(I)
250 N=M
260 NEXT I
270 GOSUB 1000
280 T=(D(N)*C(N)-A(N)*B(N))/(N*D(N)-B(N)*B(N))
290 PRINT
300 PRINT "METACENTRIC HEIGHTS IN THE ";M;"EXPERIMENTS"
310 FOR I=1 TO M
320 PRINT G(I)
330 NEXT I
340 PRINT
350 PRINT "MAX VALUE OF C OF G =",T,"MM"
360 GO TO 2000
1000 A(0)=0
1010 B(0)=0
1020 C(0)=0
1030 D(0)=0
1040 FOR K=1 TO N
1050 A(K)=A(K-1)+X(K)*Y(K)
1060 B(K)=B(K-1)+X(K)
```

```
1070 C(K)=C(K-1)+Y(K)
1080 D(K)=D(K-1)+X(K)*X(K)
1090 NEXT K
1100 RETURN
2000 END

READY


RUN

METACENT   2-JUL-81  09:20:13

ESTIMATION OF METACENTRIC HT AND LIMIT OF C OF G

TOTAL WEIGHT OF VESSEL (N)=  ? 2.5
MOVEABLE WEIGHT (N)=  ? 0.2
HOW MANY EXPERIMENTS?  ? 3
HOW MANY PAIRS OF DATA POINTS PER EXPT? ? 4

METACENTRIC HEIGHTS IN THE  3 EXPERIMENTS
  26.5463
  41.6697
  58.2669

MAX VALUE OF C OF G =       118.517    MM

READY
```

Program notes

(1) Data for the three experiments are given in lines 1–5. At lines 30–100 the total vessel weight is input as W1, the movable weight as W2, the number of experiments conducted as M and the number of data points per experiment as N.

(2) In the loop between lines 110 and 130 the first N data values (deck weight positions) are read as X(I).

(3) At line 140 a loop (extending to line 210) commences in which the running variable I identifies the particular set of experimental data being analysed. A subsidiary loop starts at line 150 (closing at line 170) and reads the next N data points (angle of tilt) as Y(I). With these X and Y values read and stored the program on the command GOSUB at line 180 goes to a subroutine commencing at line 1000.

(4) The subroutine evaluates the sums $\Sigma X(K)Y(K)$, $\Sigma X(K)$, $\Sigma Y(K)$ and $\Sigma X(K)^2$ as A(K), B(K), C(K), D(K) respectively where K runs from I to N (note that the variables A(K), B(K), C(K), D(K) are set to zero at the start to initialise the summation). When the summations have been performed the program is returned (at line 1100) to the main bloc at line 190.

(5) At line 190 the slope of the graph of angle of tilt against deck weight position is evaluated as S(I) using the equation for a least-squares fit to a set of data points (see Figure 2.14(a)) and at line 200

Example 2.4 VENTCALIB: calibration of venturi meter 33

the metacentric height is evaluated as G(I) using Equation (2.11). At line 210 the analysis of the particular experiment is completed and the procedure is repeated for the remaining experiments.

(6) The second phase of the analysis commences in the loop between lines 220 and 260 in which the remaining M data values (distance GZ) are read as Y(I), the previously evaluated G(I) values are relabelled X(I) and so that the subroutine can be accessed from line 270, N is set equal to M.

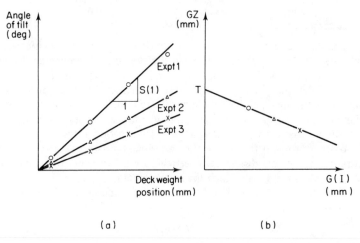

(a)   (b)

Figure 2.14(a) Angle of tilt vs Deck weight position (b) GZ vs metacentric height

(7) The subroutine output is used at line 280 to evaluate the intercept on the Y(I) (GZ) axis of the best straight line fitted through a graph of GZ vs G(I) as T (see Figure 2.14(b)).

(8) Finally, the metacentric heights for the three experiments are printed in the loop between lines 310 and 330 and the maximum permissible value of the centre of gravity of the system is printed at 350.

(9) From these results the dimensions of the toy mast height may be readily assessed.

Example 2.4 VENTCALIB: calibration of venturi meter

In an experiment to calibrate a venturi meter (Figure 2.15) the following data were obtained

W weight of water (N)	T time to collect (s)	H manometer head (m)
1000	68	0.298
1000	76	0.239
1000	85	0.191
750	73	0.147
750	81	0.119
750	101	0.075
500	84	0.048
250	54	0.030
250	88	0.012

The data refer to the weight of water W collected in a weighing tank in a certain length of time T when the pressure difference across the meter recorded by the manometer was a head H measured in metres.

The inlet pipe to the venturi was of diameter 0.0318 m and the throat of the meter was of diameter 0.0151 m. The manometer was of the mercury-water type. The experimental set-up incorporated an infinitely variable valve to allow a wide range of flow rates.

Write a program to analyse the experimental data, evaluate a representative value of discharge coefficient and present the range of Reynolds numbers over which the system operates.

The discharge measured by the venturi meter is given by the equation

$$Q_{th} = A_2 \sqrt{\left(\frac{2gh_1 \left(\frac{\rho_m}{\rho} - 1 \right)}{1 - (A_2/A_1)^2} \right)} \qquad (2.24)$$

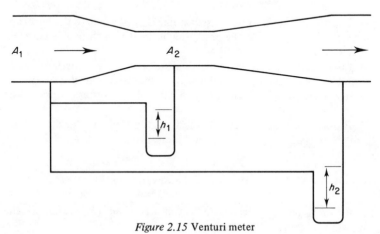

Figure 2.15 Venturi meter

Example 2.4 VENTCALIB: calibration of venturi meter   35

where A_1 is the entrance pipe area, A_2 is the throat area, ρ is the density of the flowing fluid, ρ_m is the manometer fluid density and h_1 is the manometer head between entry and throat. The theoretical discharge Q_{th} is related to the actual discharge Q_a by the discharge coefficient C_d where

$$Q_a = C_d \, Q_{th} \qquad (2.25)$$

```
LIST


VENTCALIB  2-JUL-81  09:25:07

10 PRINT "CALIBRATION OF VENTURI METER"
20 PRINT
30 PRINT "DIAMETER OF INLET PIPE (M)=  ";
40 INPUT D1
50 PRINT "DIAMETER OF THROAT (M)=   ";
60 INPUT D2
70 REM INPUT DENSITY OF MANOMETER FLUIDS
80 PRINT "DENSITY OF MERCURY/WATER IN MANOMETER (KG/M^3)";
90 INPUT R1,R2
100 PRINT "VISCOSITY OF WATER (KG/MS)=  ";
110 INPUT V
120 DATA 1000,68,.298,1000,76,0.239
130 DATA 1000,85,0.191,750,73,0.147
140 DATA 750,81,0.119,750,101,0.075
150 DATA 500,84,0.048,250,54,0.030
160 DATA 250,88,0.012
170 DIM W(20),T(20),H(20),Q(20),N(20),C(20),F(20)
180 PRINT "HOW MANY SETS OF DATA?  ";
190 INPUT N
200 PRINT
210 FOR I=1 TO N
220 READ W(I),T(I),H(I)
230 NEXT I
240 A1=PI*D1*D1/4
250 A2=PI*D2*D2/4
260 C=A2*SQR(((2*9.81*((R1/R2)-1)))/(1-(A2/A1)^2))
270 PRINT " ","Q TH","Q ACT","CD","RE NO"
280 PRINT " ","M^3/S","M^3/S"
290 PRINT "_____."
300 FOR I=1 TO N
310 Q(I)=C*SQR(H(I))
320 F(I)=W(I)/(9.81*R2*T(I))
330 C(I)=F(I)/Q(I)
340 N(I)=R2*(F(I)/A1)*D1/V
350 PRINT I,Q(I),F(I),C(I),N(I)
360 NEXT I
370 PRINT
380 S(0)=0
390 FOR I=1 TO N
400 S(I)=S(I-1)+C(I)
410 NEXT I
420 A=S(N)/N
430 PRINT "AVERAGE VALUE OF DISCHARGE COEFFICIENT =   ";
440 PRINT A
450 END

READY

RUN

VENTCALIB  2-JUL-81  09:26:01

CALIBRATION OF VENTURI METER
```

```
DIAMETER OF INLET PIPE (M)=  ? 0.0318
DIAMETER OF THROAT (M)=  ? 0.0151
DENSITY OF MERCURY/WATER IN MANOMETER (KG/M^3)? 13600,1000
VISCOSITY OF WATER (KG/MS)=  ? 1.1E-3
HOW MANY SETS OF DATA?  ? 9
```

	Q TH M^3/S	Q ACT M^3/S	CD	RE NO
1	1.57767E-03	1.49907E-03	.950179	54564.8
2	1.41289E-03	1.34127E-03	.949314	48821.1
3	1.26306E-03	1.19926E-03	.949482	43651.8
4	1.10807E-03	1.04730E-03	.945153	38120.6
5	9.96970E-04	9.43859E-04	.946728	34355.6
6	7.91479E-04	7.56957E-04	.956383	27552.5
7	6.33183E-04	6.06767E-04	.95828	22085.7
8	5.00575E-04	4.71930E-04	.942775	17177.8
9	3.16592E-04	2.89593E-04	.914722	10540.9

```
AVERAGE VALUE OF DISCHARGE COEFFICIENT =    .945891

READY
```

Program notes

(1) In response to the prompts between lines 30 and 100 the system geometry, manometer fluid characteristics and fluid viscosity are input before the data is included in the program between lines 120 and 160.

(2) The DIM statement at line 170 creates sufficient storage space for the relevant variables. Here, with nine sets of data to be read and operated on, the space available is more than adequate, with up to 20 numbers being capable of storage in the appropriate register.

(3) In the loop between lines 210 and 230 data are read in groups of three for the nine sets of data as weight of water collected W(I), time for this collection T(I) and head registered on the manometer, H(I).

(4) At lines 240 and 250 the cross-sectional areas of the inlet pipe and meter throat are calculated as A1 and A2 respectively before C is evaluated at line 260 where C represents all the system constants in Equation (2.24) which can be written:

$$Q_{th} = CH^{1/2} \qquad (2.26)$$

where Q_{th} is the theoretical discharge through the meter when a head H is registered by the manometer.

(5) After appropriate output headings have been printed (here, for theoretical discharge, actual discharge, discharge coefficient and Reynolds number), at lines 270–290 the loop between lines 300 and 360 is used to operate on each set of data in turn to evaluate theoretical discharge Q(I) for a given head H(I), actual discharge F(I) from the water collection data, discharge coefficient C(I) as the ratio of actual to theoretical discharge and Reynolds number N(I) based on flow conditions in the inlet pipe. The results of each analysis are printed at line 350.

Example 2.5 SPHEREDRG: evaluation of drag coefficient   37

(6) In order to average the calculated value of discharge coefficient the variable S(I) is initially set to zero at line 380 and in the loop between lines 390 and 410 the nine values of discharge coefficient are added up before (at line 420) they are averaged as A and printed at line 440.

(7) The results indicate an average value of C_d of 0.95. This figure, which is less than unity as a result of the small energy loss which occurs in the convergent section of the meter between pressure tappings, is a little lower than might normally be expected (a figure of about 0.98 is usual) and would indicate that some maintenance on the system might be desirable. This could include ensuring that manometer pipes are clean and free of sediment and that there has been no build-up of material (rusting, etc.) in the meter itself.

Example 2.5 SPHEREDRG: evaluation of drag coefficient

As part of an experiment to investigate the drag force on different shaped bodies a sphere was attached to a drag balance and suspended at the centre of the working section of a large cross-section, low-speed wind-tunnel capable of producing a maximum air velocity of approximately 40 m/s. Readings of drag force in newtons over the whole tunnel speed range were made as shown below

Drag (N)	H (mm)
0.16	1.50
0.38	3.38
0.64	6.02
0.98	9.40
1.38	13.51
1.80	18.39
3.29	24.03
2.78	30.48
3.20	37.59
2.85	45.47
1.62	54.10
1.89	63.50
2.14	73.60
2.40	84.58
2.71	96.01

H is the head measured on a water-filled manometer connected between the wall of the working section and atmosphere. The sphere, which was of diameter 0.1524 m was smooth during the course of the test detailed above but could readily be artificially roughened by means of a small annulus of adhesive tape stuck onto the front part of the body. The atmospheric pressure at which the experiment was conducted was 755 mm of mercury and the temperature was 17.5°C.

The following program analyses the experimental data to yield a table of drag coefficients and Reynolds numbers.

```
LIST


SPHEREDRG  8-JUL-81  14:49:04

10 PRINT "EVALUATION OF SPHERE DRAG COEFFICIENT"
20 PRINT
30 PRINT "IS DATA FOR SMOOTH OR ROUGH SPHERE?"
40 PRINT "-----------"
50 INPUT A$
60 PRINT "-----------"
70 DIM C(25),F(25),H(25),R(25),U(25)
80 PRINT
90 PRINT
100 PRINT "NUMBER OF SETS OF DATA=   ";
110 INPUT N
120 PRINT "DIAMETER OF SPHERE (M)=   ";
130 INPUT D
140 PRINT "AMBIENT TEMPERATURE DURING THE EXPERIMENT (DEG C)=   ";
150 INPUT T
160 PRINT "ATMOSPHERIC PRESSURE DURING THE EXPERIMENT (MM HG)=    ";
170 INPUT P
180 R=P*13.6*9.81/(287.1*(T+273))
190 PRINT "DENSITY OF AIR UNDER THESE CONDITIONS (KG/M^3)="R
200 REM EVALUATE DYNAMIC VISCOSITY OF AIR USING SUTHERLANDS FORMULA
220 V=1.46000E-06*((T+273)^1.5)/(T+387)
230 PRINT "DYNAMIC VISCOSITY OF AIR UNDER THESE CONDITIONS (KG/MS)=";V
240 PRINT
250 PRINT "AIR VEL","DRAG F","DRAG","RE NO"
260 PRINT "M/S","N","COEFF"," "
270 PRINT "--------------------------------------------------------"
280 FOR I=1 TO N
290 READ H(I),F(I)
300 U(I)=SQR((H(I)*9.81)/(.5*R))
310 C(I)=F(I)/(.5*R*U(I)^2*(.25*PI*D^2))
320 R(I)=R*U(I)*D/V
330 PRINT U(I),F(I),C(I),R(I)
340 NEXT I
360 DATA 1.50,0.16,3.38,0.38,6.02,0.64,9.40,0.98,13.51,1.38,18.39,1.80
370 DATA 24.03,2.29,30.48,2.78,37.59,3.2,45.47,2.85,54.1,1.62,63.50,1.89
380 DATA 73.60,2.14,84.58,2.40,96.01,2.71
390 END

READY


RUN


SPHEREDRG  8-JUL-81  14:49:57

EVALUATION OF SPHERE DRAG COEFFICIENT

IS DATA FOR SMOOTH OR ROUGH SPHERE?
------------
? SMOOTH
------------


NUMBER OF SETS OF DATA=   ? 15
DIAMETER OF SPHERE (M)=   ? 0.1524
AMBIENT TEMPERATURE DURING THE EXPERIMENT (DEG C)=   ? 17.5
ATMOSPHERIC PRESSURE DURING THE EXPERIMENT (MM HG)=    ? 755
```

Example 2.5 SPHEREDRG: evaluation of drag coefficient   39

```
DENSITY OF AIR UNDER THESE CONDITIONS (KG/M^3)= 1.20775
DYNAMIC VISCOSITY OF AIR UNDER THESE CONDITIONS (KG/MS)= 1.78712E-05
```

AIR VEL M/S	DRAG F N	DRAG COEFF	RE NO
4.93637	.16	.596074	50841
7.41003	.38	.628258	76318
9.88917	.64	.594093	101851
12.3574	.98	.582599	127272
14.8146	1.38	.570815	152580
17.2843	1.8	.546968	178016
19.7578	2.29	.532541	203491
22.252	2.78	.509684	229180
24.7114	3.2	.475717	254510
27.1784	2.85	.350261	279918
29.6456	1.62	.167336	305329
32.118	1.89	.166326	330792
34.5781	2.14	.162483	356129
37.0677	2.4	.158568	381771
39.493	2.71	.157734	406749

```
READY
```

Program notes

(1) In order to identify whether the sphere is smooth or rough this information is input in the form of a string variable A$ at line 50 in response to the prompt at line 30.

(2) The DIM statement at line 70 makes enough spaces (up to 25) to accommodate the various parameters related to each set of data. The number of such sets is input at line 110, the sphere diameter is input at line 130 and atmospheric temperature and pressure are input at lines 150 and 170 as N, D, T and P respectively.

(3) Using the ideal gas equation

$$P/\rho = RT \tag{2.27}$$

where P, ρ and T are gas pressure, density and temperature respectively and R is the gas constant, the density of the air in the experiment is calculated at line 180 and printed at line 190.

(4) The remark REM at line 200 indicates that the Sutherland formula for the evaluation of dynamic viscosity of the air (a quantity which is temperature dependent) is to be used at line 220, the result being printed at line 230.

(5) Following the printout of the required headings the loop between lines 280 and 340 evaluates drag coefficient and Reynolds number for the N sets of data. Data are read in pairs as manometer head and drag force at line 290. The pressure difference, ΔP, measured by the manometer head is used to calculate air velocity U from the equation

$$\Delta P = H\rho_{water} g = \frac{1}{2} \rho_{air} U^2 \tag{2.28}$$

Drag coefficient is defined as

$$C_D = {}^1F/\tfrac{1}{2}\,\rho U^2 A \qquad (2.29)$$

where A is the cross-sectional area of the sphere and is evaluated at line 310. Reynolds number based on sphere diameter is found at line 320 and the results printed at line 330.

(6) The results can be plotted in two ways, either as drag force against air velocity or non-dimensionally as drag coefficient against Reynolds number as shown in Figure 2.16. On both graphs an important feature

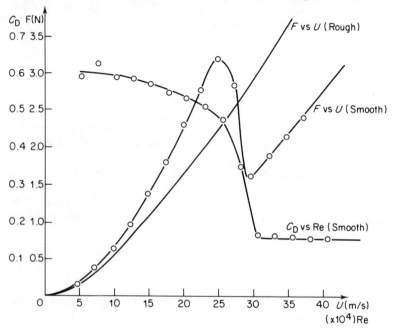

Figure 2.16 C_d vs Re and D vs U

is the sudden drop in drag and drag coefficient at a particular speed and Reynolds number. This is explained by considering the boundary layers that develop over the surface of the sphere. At low Reynolds numbers the boundary layer is laminar and consequently separates from the sphere at about 90° in a similar way to that shown in the Figure 2.11(a). This causes a wide wake downstream of the sphere. A wake represents a loss of fluid momentum and as a consequence a high drag force acting on the sphere. As speed, and hence Reynolds number, increases the laminar boundary layer undergoes transition to a turbulent layer which separates later than previously at about 120° as shown in Figure 2.11(b). The wake is consequently narrower and the drag force is reduced.

Experiments conducted on a sphere artificially roughened as described above would indicate that a turbulent boundary layer forms even at low Reynolds numbers and the drag here would be less than the smooth case. There would be no transition and at high Reynolds numbers the drag would be in excess of the smooth sphere drag by virtue of the roughness attached to the body. (See Figure 2.16).

PROBLEMS

(2.1) An inclined tube manometer, similar to that shown in Figure 2.3(a) is used to measure the pressure difference across an orifice plate which monitors the volume flow rate through a circular air duct. Because a wide range of flows is possible, the manometer can be adjusted to a variety of different inclinations so as to obtain the most accurate assessment of pressure drop across the plate. Write a program capable of converting the manometer scale reading (in mm) to pressure (in N/m^2) for a series of different tube inclinations if the manometer fluid is oil with specific gravity 0.784. The following represent typical data from the system.

Inclination of manometer to horizontal (degrees)	Scale reading (mm)
30	20
	40
	100
	150
60	75
	100
	140
	200
90	100
	150
	200
	250

(2.2) Because the governing equation for theoretical discharge is the same for venturi meter, flow nozzle and orifice plate, the same program could be used to analyse experimental data from all three devices. Further information that would be of interest for each of the pieces of equipment is the quantity known as meter loss factor, k, given by

$$k = |(\rho_m - \rho)gh/\tfrac{1}{2}\rho U^2 \qquad (2.30)$$

where ρ_m is manometer fluid density, ρ is working fluid density, h is the total head drop across the device and U is the mean pipe velocity.

Meter loss factor may be thought of as the fraction of dynamic fluid head lost through the meter. By modifying the program given in Example 2.4 to include the extra head drop across the meter, evaluate discharge coefficients and loss factors for a flow nozzle and an orifice plate for which the following obtains

For both devices, entrance diameter   31.8 mm
                  throat diameter   15.1 mm

Pressure drops measured by mercury-water manometers are h_1, the drop between inlet and throat and h_2, the drop across the whole instrument (see Figure 2.15).

Flow nozzle		Weight of water collected (N)	Time (s)
h_1 (m)	h_2 (m)		
0.266	0.174	1000	72
0.211	0.140	1000	81
0.163	0.108	1000	92
0.133	0.088	1000	103
0.099	0.066	800	94
0.069	0.046	600	86
0.036	0.024	600	118

Orifice plate		Weight of water collected (N)	Time (s)
h_1 (m)	h_2 (m)		
0.249	0.195	1000	111
0.199	0.156	1000	125
0.148	0.115	800	117
0.124	0.097	700	111
0.084	0.065	600	116
0.061	0.047	400	92
0.037	0.029	300	87

(2.3) Balloons are to be used to lift packages of scientific instruments to monitor atmospheric conditions. Three different balloons are available of diameters 8, 12 and 16 m. The mass of each empty balloon and its lifting equipment may be taken as 50 kg. In order to give the balloons buoyancy they are to be inflated either with helium gas (whose density may be taken as 0.178 kg/m^3) or with hydrogen gas (density 0.090 kg/m^3). The density of air may be taken as 1.225 kg/m^3. Write a program to evaluate the maximum lifting capacities of the three balloons when filled with either helium or hydrogen.

(2.4) A sharp-crested weir is a device often used in laboratories to measure the discharge of an open channel. The rectangular weir and the V-notch are the most common types and are illustrated in Figure 4.6(b). The theoretical discharge over a rectangular weir is given by

$$Q = \frac{2}{3} B\sqrt{(2g)} \, H^{3/2} \tag{2.31}$$

where B is the breadth of the weir and H is the total head above the weir. For a V-notch the discharge is given by

$$Q = \frac{8}{15} \sqrt{(2g)} \tan (\theta/2) H^{5/2} \tag{2.32}$$

where θ is the notch angle.

Write a program to evaluate the theoretical discharge over each weir if the dynamic head component of H is considered negligible and H is taken to be the height of water above the sill of the weir. Calculate discharge for static heads of 10 mm up to 90 mm in steps of 10 mm for a rectangular weir of breadth 30 m and a V-notch of total included angle 30°, if each is installed at the end of a rectangular channel of breadth 75 mm and the lowest point of each weir is 30 mm above the channel base.

(2.5) For a more accurate assessment of channel discharge using a plate weir the approach velocity and therefore the dynamic head contribution to total head is significant. The term H in the discharge equations should include both static and dynamic components of head. In order to allow the inclusion of both terms in the evaluation of discharge, an estimate of flow velocity must be made. This can be done by taking the discharge estimate obtained from static head alone, dividing it by channel upstream cross-sectional area (for the channel of Problem 2.4 this is $75 \times (h + 30)$ mm^2 where h mm is the static head over the weir) to obtain an estimate of approach velocity, V, and then forming the dynamic head $V^2/2g$ which is added to h and used in the discharge equation again to find a more accurate value. This process should be repeated until successive values of discharge for a given static head are considered sufficiently close to each other.

Write a program to compare the discharge over the rectangular weir and V-notch of Problem 2.4 in which the head used in the discharge equation is total head.

(2.6) A dam is to be constructed across a river gorge. It is to be a right-angled triangle in section with its wetted face AB vertical and hypotonuse BC downstream. When completed it will be 200 m wide. The dam is to be of reinforced concrete construction and four designs have been submitted which may be considered as having four distinct average densities of 2000, 2250, 2600 and 3000 kg/m^3. The base of the dam cannot, for topographical and geological reasons, extend further than 100 m downstream of face AB. It is, of course, essential that, whatever head is impounded by the dam, the structure does not become unstable. This may simply be thought of as a pivotting motion about the toe of the dam C caused by the hydrostatic pressure force moment exceeding the restoring moment due to the dam weight.

The main governing factor in determining the exact geometry and structure of the dam is the cost of the structure which is given by the formula £(0.8 − 0.0002ρ) per cubic metre of finished dam where ρ is the density of the fabric.

Investigate the dimensions and cost of the possible solutions and calculate what heads of water will be impounded.

(2.7)   Water flows in a square duct of 800 mm internal dimension. A pitot tube sited in the middle of one of the walls of the duct is traversed across the section in order to establish the distribution of velocity across the section. When the pressure readings from the pitot tube are converted to velocities the following figures result

Distance from wall (mm)	Velocity (m/s)
25	0.250
75	0.380
125	0.430
175	0.470
225	0.480
275	0.487
325	0.495
375	0.500

Write a program to evaluate the flow rate in the duct and the mean flow velocity which may be defined as flow rate divided by duct cross-sectional area. The flow may be considered symmetrical in the duct with the velocity measured at a given distance from the wall the same for each of the four faces.

(2.8)   When fluid flowing in a pipe enters a bend there will be a resultant force exerted by the pipe walls on the water causing it to deflect. There will also, of course, be an equal and opposite force on the bend itself which must be adequately restrained by external clamps and brackets, etc.

Write a program that can be used to evaluate the forces on pipe-bends (which can have both different tapers and different turning angles).

Modify the program to show that 12 retaining bolts are needed on a nozzle of 100 mm diameter discharging to atmosphere which is attached by a flange to a 400 mm diameter horizontal pipe if the

pressure in the pipe is 8 bar gauge and each bolt can resist a tensile
load of 8 kN.

(2.9) A cylindrical oil pipeline is to be laid from a drilling platform in
the North Sea to a refinery on the mainland. Since the pipeline will be
subjected to strong currents producing significant drag forces a model
of the pipeline is to be tested in a wind tunnel to determine its drag
characteristics in an equivalent flow. A pressure tapping was made in a
small model cylinder which spanned the wind tunnel and could be
rotated in the stream. The results from the pressure readings gave the
following values of pressure coefficient C_p (defined as $(p - p_0)/\frac{1}{2}\rho V^2 d$,
where p is the pressure measured by the tapping, p_0 is the static
pressure in the tunnel, ρ is air density, V is free stream velocity and d
is cylinder diameter) for various angles of the tapping to the oncoming
flow

Angle (degrees)	C_p
0	1.00
20	0.70
40	−0.15
60	−1.00
80	−1.12
100	−0.98
120	−0.98
140	−1.04
160	−1.10
180	−1.11

From these data evaluate the drag coefficient C_D (defined as $F/\frac{1}{2}\rho U^2 d$
where F is drag force on the cylinder) which is related to pressure coefficient by the equation

$$C_D = \int_0^\pi C_p \cos \theta \, d\theta \qquad (2.33)$$

where θ is the angle measured from the leading point of the cylinder.

Chapter 3

Flow in pipes and pipe networks

ESSENTIAL THEORY

3.1 Introduction

When fluid flows in a pipe it is subjected to a frictional drag force at the pipe wall. To sustain flow it is necessary to maintain a decrease in pressure in the direction of flow. The friction and pressure forces require evaluation so that, for instance, pumps of sufficient power may be provided to ensure efficient drainage of a construction site or adequate head is available to generate the required power from turbines in a hydro-electric project. Problems arise when fluid is accelerated or decelerated in a pipe. Such unsteady flow gives rise to extremes of pressure which may require the incorporation of safety devices to prevent system failure. In this chapter the equations governing both steady and unsteady pipe flows are presented together with several problems related to their use.

3.2 Fully developed flow

Fluid entering a pipe from a large reservoir has an initially uniform velocity distribution across the whole pipe. Wall friction causes thickening boundary layers to form on the pipe which alter this velocity distribution. Eventually these boundary layers meet at the centre of the pipe. Downstream of this point the velocity profile remains unaltered and flow is described as fully developed. If the Reynolds number of the flow (based on the mean flow velocity and pipe diameter, Vd/ν, where ν is the fluid kinematic viscosity) is below 2000, laminar flow develops fully in a pipe length of about 50 diameters. At Reynolds numbers in excess of this value turbulent flow will develop in a somewhat shorter entrance length (Figure 3.1). In fully developed flow the head lost due to friction between two stations along the pipe is given by

$$h_f = 4 \tau_0 L/\rho dg \qquad (3.1)$$

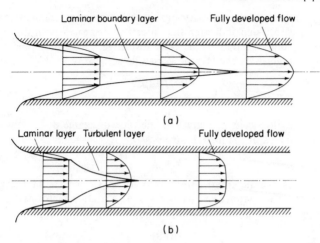

Figure 3.1(a) Development of laminar pipe flow (b) Development of turbulent pipe flow [after Massey, *Mechanics of Fluids* 3rd ed., Van Nostrand Reinhold, (1975)]

where τ_0 is the wall shear stress, L is the distance between stations, ρ is the fluid density, d is pipe diameter and g is gravitational acceleration. By using the non-dimensional friction factor

$$f = \tau_0 / \tfrac{1}{2}\rho V^2 \qquad (3.2)$$

the head loss equation, known as the Darcy—Weisbach formula is written

$$h_f = \frac{4fL}{d} \cdot \frac{V^2}{2g} \qquad (3.3)$$

In the case of non-circular ducts this expression becomes

$$h_f = \frac{fL}{m} \cdot \frac{V^2}{2g} \qquad (3.4)$$

where m is the duct hydraulic radius defined as cross-sectional area divided by duct perimeter. (For a circular pipe $m = d/4$.)

3.3   Laminar and turbulent flow in smooth pipes

For laminar flow in a circular pipe the velocity v at a radius r from the centre of the pipe is given by

$$v = \frac{1}{4\mu}\left(-\frac{dp}{dx}\right)\left(R^2 - r^2\right) \qquad (3.5)$$

where μ is fluid dynamic viscosity, dp/dx is the pressure gradient in the pipe (the negative sign indicates that pressure decreases with distance) and R is the pipe internal radius. The discharge, Q, from a pipe with laminar flow is given by the Hagen–Poiseuille equation

$$Q = \frac{\pi R^4}{8\mu} \left(-\frac{dp}{dx} \right) \tag{3.6}$$

and the mean flow velocity, equal to the pipe discharge divided by the cross-sectional area of the pipe, is given by

$$V = \tfrac{1}{2} v_{max} \tag{3.7}$$

where v_{max} is the maximum fluid velocity at the centre of the pipe calculated from Equation (3.5) when $r = 0$. The friction factor as defined in Equation (3.2) in laminar flow is given by

$$f = 16/Re \tag{3.8}$$

where Re is the Reynolds number of the flow, defined above.

In turbulent flow the velocity at any point in the pipe is not constant but may be regarded as being composed of a steady time-averaged velocity on which a fluctuating component caused by eddying is super-imposed. By application of the mixing length theory (due to Prandtl) the universal velocity distribution in turbulent pipe flow which gives the velocity v, at a distance y from the pipe is written

$$v/v^* = A \log_{10} yv^*/v + B \tag{3.9}$$

where v^* is called friction velocity ($=(\tau_0/\rho)^{1/2}$) and A and B are experimentally derived constants found to be 5.75 and 5.5 respectively. Very close to the wall this law breaks down and flow is laminar in a region known as the laminar sublayer where velocity is given by

$$v/v^*_i = yv^*/v \tag{3.10}$$

Thus, in turbulent flow, the velocity profile is as shown in Figure 3.2.

Further analysis of Equation (3.9) yields an expression for friction factor of the form

$$1/\sqrt{f} = 4 \log_{10}(Re\sqrt{f}) - 0.4 \tag{3.11}$$

known as the universal pipe friction law. This somewhat complex expression (requiring an iterative method of solving for f for a given value of Re) is sometimes replaced by the empirical formula due to Blasius

$$f = 0.0791/Re^{1/4} \tag{3.12}$$

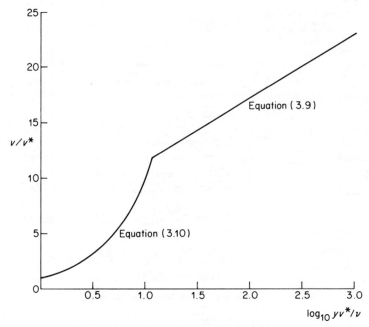

Figure 3.2 Universal velocity law for smooth pipes

3.4 Flow in rough pipes

The preceding remarks apply to smooth pipes. When there is a significant roughness on the inside of the pipe there is little effect on laminar flow unless the surface irregularities constitute an appreciable change in pipe diameter. Friction factor can still be evaluated from Equation (3.8). In turbulent flow the effect of surface roughness on the velocity profile is determined by the relative heights of the roughness and the laminar sublayer. If the irregularities stay submerged in the sublayer then the pipe remains hydraulically smooth. If these roughnesses emerge from the layer then additional turbulence and pressure drag is created and friction factor increases. Generally, friction factor in turbulent flow is given by

$$f = \phi[\mathrm{Re}, k/d] \tag{3.13}$$

where k is the mean roughness height. Nikuradse carried out tests on artificially roughened pipes using sand grains to discover the form of the function ϕ. This work was extended by Moody who used an 'equivalent' sand grain roughness to investigate the behaviour of commercial pipes. Moody's diagram, Figure 3.3, is now widely used for such pipes. Moody also developed an approximate formula for friction factor, accurate to

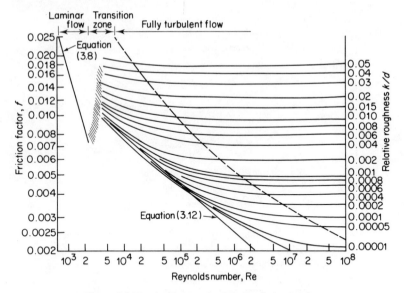

Figure 3.3 Moody diagram for friction factor in pipes

within 5% for Reynolds numbers between 4000 and 10 000 000 and relative roughnesses, k/d, of less than 0.1 of the form

$$f = 0.001375 \left[1 + (20\,000 \frac{k}{d} + \frac{10^6}{Re})^{1/3} \right] \qquad (3.14)$$

This equation is somewhat easier to handle than that which Moody used to construct Figure 3.3, known as the Colebrook–White formula of the form

$$\frac{1}{\sqrt{f}} = -4 \log_{10} \left(\frac{k}{3.71d} + \frac{1.26}{Re\sqrt{f}} \right) \qquad (3.15)$$

3.5 Localised head losses

Wherever a pipe-system contains bends, changes in cross-sectional area or fittings such as valves, etc., additional head losses are introduced which can generally be written as

$$h_L = K(V^2/2g) \qquad (3.16)$$

where K is a head loss coefficient associated with the feature (e.g. for a sharp entrance to a pipe $K = 0.5$ and for an abrupt exit $K = 1.0$).

3.6 Network analysis

It is sometimes desirable to plot the variation of head throughout a pipe system by means of total head lines, where total head is given relative to some datum level. A simple example is shown in Figure 3.4.

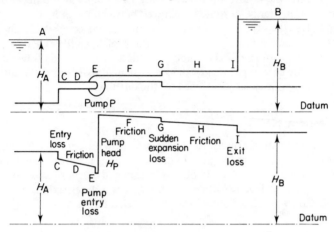

Figure 3.4 Changes in head in a pipe system

In a network of pipes in which flow from a given inlet to a given outflow point may come via several different routes (as shown in Figure 3.5) then analysis using Bernoulli's equation to solve for individual pipe flows and head changes would result in a large number of simultaneous equations. The usual approach to such a problem is to use a method based on obtaining successive approximations to the real solution.

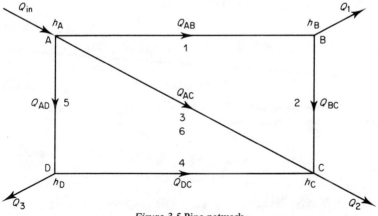

Figure 3.5 Pipe network

When the total volume flow is known but the heads at pipe junctions are unknown (h_A, h_B, h_C and h_D in Figure 3.5), the method of head balancing is used. Flows are assumed for the separate pipes of the network (Q_{AB}, Q_{BC}, Q_{AC}, Q_{AD} and Q_{DC} in Figure 3.5) and successively adjusted until the head drop between any two points in the network is the same, no matter what route is followed between the points.

Similarly, when the heads at various points in the network are known but flow quantities are not, the method of quantity balancing is employed. An estimate of the junction heads is made and the flow rate is calculated for each pipe. Head values are then adjusted until the inflow to each junction is exactly balanced by the outflow.

3.7   Unsteady pipe flow

The foregoing remarks apply to steady pipe flow. When fluid is accelerated or decelerated in a pipe (e.g. by closing a valve) considerable pressure changes can occur. If fluid is considered to move as an incompressible 'plug' of length L then if it undergoes a deceleration dv/dt the pressure difference that results from this deceleration is

$$dp = \rho L \frac{dv}{dt} \tag{3.17}$$

When the deceleration becomes very large (when a valve is closed very rapidly) Equation (3.17) is no longer valid. The fluid is compressed and the pressure change propagates as a shock wave travelling through the fluid in the pipe. When this occurs in, say, a domestic water supply the wave produces a heavy knocking sound known as water hammer.

If the pipe is made of rigid material then the speed of the shock wave is the same as the speed of sound in the fluid

$$c = \sqrt{K/\rho} \tag{3.18}$$

where K is the fluid bulk modulus of elasticity. The accompanying pressure rise is

$$dp = V \sqrt{(\rho K)} \tag{3.19}$$

where V is the mean fluid velocity before closure. When the pipe is itself elastic then shock speed is given by

$$c = \sqrt{\left[\frac{1}{\rho \left(\dfrac{1}{K} + \dfrac{d}{t\,E} \right)} \right]} \tag{3.20}$$

where d is pipe diameter, t is pipe wall thickness and E is Young's modulus of the pipe material.

For a pipe of length L, when the wave reaches the far end it will reflect and return to the closed end in a time given by

$$t = 2L/c \qquad (3.21)$$

(known as a pipe period) where it will undergo a further pressure step equal to $-2.dp$ as shown in Figure 3.6 for a pipe leading from a reservoir. This reflection process will continue with positive and negative pressure steps that gradually decay in amplitude as friction degrades the fluid kinetic energy to heat.

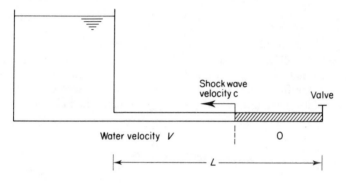

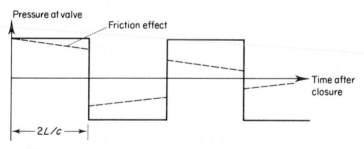

Figure 3.6 Propagation of water hammer wave and valve pressure profile

In order to reduce the size of the pressure waves generated by sudden valve closure the time of closure is increased to a period in excess of 8–10 pipe periods. If a valve is assumed to close linearly in time T such that the area through which flow occurs is given by

$$A = A_0 \left(1 - \frac{t}{T}\right) \qquad (3.22)$$

where A_0 is the flow area prior to closure then the velocity in the pipe at time t is given by

$$V = V_0 \sqrt{\left(\frac{H}{H_R}\right)} \left(1 - \frac{t}{T}\right) \tag{3.23}$$

where V_0 is the initial pipe fluid velocity, H is the head behind the valve and H_R is the head initially (equal to the valve head at $t = 0$). In this case the maximum head behind the valve is given by

$$H_{max}/H_R = 1 + \frac{1}{2}a^2 + a^2 \sqrt{\left(\frac{1}{4} + \frac{1}{a^2}\right)} \tag{3.24}$$

where

$$a = V_0 L/gTH_R \tag{3.25}$$

(L is the length of the pipe.)

In a hydro-electric scheme in which large volumes of water are accelerated and decelerated, surge tanks are incorporated in the system to protect the flow ducts from excess pressure rises and to allow rapid start-up of the system to avoid wastage of valuable fluid (Figure 3.7).

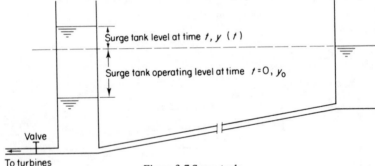

Figure 3.7 Surge tank

When a system is closed down, instead of a shock wave propagating back to the reservoir, fluid is caused to flow into the surge tank. The level in the surge tank relative to the reservoir surface is given by the equation

$$y + Kv \, |v| = -\frac{L}{g} \cdot \frac{dv}{dt} \tag{3.26}$$

where v is the duct velocity at time t. Solution of this equation with the continuity equation for the system

$$av = A \frac{dy}{dt} \tag{3.27}$$

where a is the duct cross-sectional area and A is the surge tank area, allows the water level at any time to be computed and hence an

Example 3.1 FRICFACT: comparison of pipe friction factors   55

economical surge tank design to be evolved. K is a factor which accounts for any frictional and other losses in the system.

WORKED EXAMPLES

Example 3.1 FRICFACT: comparison of pipe friction factors

Equation (3.11) gives an expression for smooth pipe friction factor in terms of Reynolds number. This equation is derived from the universal velocity distribution law. A somewhat simpler empirical expression due to Blasius is given by Equation (3.12). In order to investigate the range of validity of the Blasius equation, solve these two equations for a given Reynolds number and hence suggest in what Reynolds number regime Equation (3.12) may be considered valid.

```
LIST

FRICFACT    2-JUL-81  16:04:18

10 PRINT "COMPARISON OF FRICTION FACTOR VALUES DERIVED FROM"
20 PRINT "BLASIUS EQUATION AND UNIVERSAL VELOCITY DISTRIBUTION LAW"
30 PRINT
40 DATA 1000,1500,2000,2500,3000,3500,4000,4500,5000,5500,6000
45 DATA 6500,7000,7500,8000,8500,9000,9500,10000,15000,20000,25000
50 DATA 30000,35000,40000,45000,50000,55000,60000,65000,70000
55 DATA 75000,80000,85000,90000,95000,100000,150000,200000,250000
60 DATA 300000,350000,400000,450000,500000,550000,600000,650000
70 PRINT "HOW MANY REYNOLDS NUMBER VALUES?    ",
80 INPUT N
90 DIM R(50)
100 PRINT
110 PRINT "RE NO","UNIV VEL","BLASIUS","%"
120 PRINT " ","DIST F"," F ","DIFF"
125 PRINT "-----------------------------------------------------"
130 F=.0175
140 FOR I=1 TO N
150 READ R(I)
160 E=SQR(F)
170 A=4*.4343*LOG(R(I)*E)-.4
180 B=1/E
190 C=A-B
200 IF ABS(C)<.05 THEN 230
210 F=F-2.50000E-05
220 GO TO 160
230 F1=.0791/R(I)^.25
240 D=ABS(100*(1-F/F1))
250 PRINT R(I),F,F1,D
260 NEXT I
270 END

READY


RUN


FRICFACT    2-JUL-81  16:05:01

COMPARISON OF FRICTION FACTOR VALUES DERIVED FROM
BLASIUS EQUATION AND UNIVERSAL VELOCITY DISTRIBUTION LAW
```

```
HOW MANY REYNOLDS NUMBER VALUES?          ? 48

RE NO        UNIV VEL        BLASIUS       %
             DIST F          F             DIFF
------------------------------------------------------
  1000       .015825         .0140662      12.5036
  1500       .0137249        .0127102      7.98332
  2000       .0124749        .0118282      5.46747
  2500       .0116249        .0111864      3.91966
  3000       .0109749        .010688       2.68427
  3500       .0104749        .0102839      1.85668
  4000       .0100499        9.94630E-03   1.04133
  4500       9.72487E-03     9.65769E-03   .695562
  5000       9.42486E-03     9.40663E-03   .193846
  5500       9.17486E-03     9.18514E-03   .111932
  6000       8.94985E-03     8.98749E-03   .4188
  6500       8.74985E-03     8.80943E-03   .676358
  7000       8.57485E-03     8.64773E-03   .842738
  7500       8.39984E-03     8.49985E-03   1.17652
  8000       8.24984E-03     8.36381E-03   1.36259
  8500       8.12484E-03     8.23800E-03   1.37362
  9000       7.99984E-03     8.12112E-03   1.49339
  9500       7.87484E-03     8.01209E-03   1.71304
 10000       7.77483E-03     7.91000E-03   1.70879
 15000       6.99984E-03     7.14749E-03   2.06583
 20000       6.49984E-03     6.65149E-03   2.27996
 25000       6.17484E-03     6.29059E-03   1.84009
 30000       5.89984E-03     6.01030E-03   1.83784
 35000       5.69984E-03     5.78308E-03   1.43946
 40000       5.52484E-03     5.59321E-03   1.22249
 45000       5.37484E-03     5.43092E-03   1.03261
 50000       5.24984E-03     5.28973E-03   .754213
 55000       5.12484E-03     5.16518E-03   .781101
 60000       5.04984E-03     5.05404E-03   .0831008
 65000       4.94984E-03     4.95391E-03   .0821829
 70000       4.87484E-03     4.86297E-03   .243998
 75000       4.79984E-03     4.77982E-03   .418913
 80000       4.72484E-03     4.70331E-03   .45768
 85000       4.67484E-03     4.63257E-03   .912499
 90000       4.62484E-03     4.56684E-03   1.27001
 95000       4.57484E-03     4.50553E-03   1.53842
100000       4.52484E-03     4.44812E-03   1.72478
150000       4.14984E-03     4.01933E-03   3.24706
200000       3.92484E-03     3.74041E-03   4.93083
250000       3.74984E-03     3.53746E-03   6.00381
300000       3.62484E-03     3.37984E-03   7.24891
350000       3.52484E-03     3.25207E-03   8.38776
400000       3.42484E-03     3.14530E-03   8.88778
450000       3.34984E-03     3.05403E-03   9.68598
500000       3.29984E-03     2.97464E-03   10.9326
550000       3.24984E-03     2.90460E-03   11.8862
600000       3.19984E-03     2.84210E-03   12.5874
650000       3.14984E-03     2.78579E-03   13.0682

READY
```

Program notes

(1) Values of Reynolds number from below the threshold of laminar flow (Re = 2000) up to 10^6 are input as data in lines 40–60.

(2) An initial value of friction factor F is given as 0.0175, a value somewhat greater than the Blasius prediction for Re = 1000.

(3) The loop between lines 140 and 260 reads the appropriate Reynolds number figure from data and then evaluates the right hand side of

Example 3.2 PIPEFITTG: local losses at pipe fittings   57

Equation (3.11) as A and the left hand side as B for the starting value of F. A and B are compared and if they differ by more than 0.05 then F is reduced by $2.5.10^{-5}$ at line 210 before the process is repeated. When a satisfactory F value is found the Blasius equation is used to evaluate the other friction factor value as F1 and the results are printed together with a comparison between the two values.

(4) A new Reynolds number value is read and the F-value just printed is used to initiate the solution.

(5) Smaller steps in F and a narrower tolerance band may be used to obtain a more accurate iterated solution.

(6) From the tabulated output it would seem reasonable to apply the Blasius approximate Equation (3.12) in the Reynolds number regime from 3000 up to 100 000 where the two friction factor values differ by less than 3%.

Example 3.2 PIPEFITTG: local losses at pipe fittings

As well as the losses due to friction in a pipe, localised losses associated with a fitting or a particular feature of the pipe-line can cause quite significant head decrements.

The program below is the beginning of what could be a comprehensive directory for the losses incurred at various pipe fixtures, commencing with the head lost at an abrupt entrance, exit and at a sudden enlargement. The program is capable of extension to include a wide variety of different geometries and flow conditions.

```
PIPEFITTG   2-JUL-81  16:07:35

10 PRINT "LOCAL LOSSES AT PIPE FITTINGS"
20 PRINT "TYPE OF FITTING"
30 PRINT "_____"
40 PRINT "ABRUPT ENTRANCE (1)"
50 PRINT "ABRUPT EXIT (2)"
60 PRINT "SUDDEN ENLARGEMENT(3)"
70 PRINT "_____"
80 PRINT
90 PRINT "SELECT FITTING BY INPUTTING CODE NUMBER";
100 INPUT A
110 PRINT
120 PRINT "PIPE DISCHARGE(M^3/S)=";
130 INPUT Q
140 PRINT
150 IF A=1 GO TO 210
160 IF A=2 GO TO 290
170 IF A=3 GO TO 370
180 PRINT "PIPE DIAMETER  (M)=";
190 INPUT D1
200 PRINT
210 PRINT "ABRUPT ENTRANCE, K=1"
220 PRINT "_____"
230 PRINT "DOWNSTREAM PIPE DIAMETER (M)=";
240 INPUT D1
250 H1=1*(Q/(PI*D1^2/4))^2/(2*9.81)
260 PRINT "HEADLOSS (M)=";
```

```
270 PRINT H1
280 GO TO 470
290 PRINT "ABRUPT EXIT, K=0.5"
300 PRINT "------------------------------"
310 PRINT "UPSTREAM PIPE DIAMETER (M)=";
320 INPUT D1
330 H2=.5*(Q/(PI*D1^2/4))^2/(2*9.81)
340 PRINT "HEADLOSS (M)=";
350 PRINT H2
360 GO TO 470
370 PRINT "SUDDEN ENLARGEMENT, K=(1-(D1/D2)^2)"
380 PRINT "------------------------------------------"
390 PRINT "UPSTREAM PIPE DIAMETER (M)=";
400 INPUT D1
410 PRINT "DOWNSTREAM DIAMETER (M)=";
420 INPUT D2
430 PRINT "HEADLOSS (M)=";
440 H3=(1-(D1/D2)^2)*(Q/(PI*D1^2/4))^2/(2*9.81)
450 PRINT H3
460 GO TO 470
470 PRINT
480 PRINT "ANY FURTHER FITTINGS ETC? (Y/N)";
490 INPUT A$
500 IF A$="Y" GO TO 30
510 END

READY


PIPEFITTG  3-JUL-81  14:27:50

LOCAL LOSSES AT PIPE FITTINGS
TYPE OF FITTING
------------------------------
ABRUPT ENTRANCE (1)
ABRUPT EXIT (2)
SUDDEN ENLARGEMENT(3)
------------------------------

SELECT FITTING BY INPUTTING CODE NUMBER? 1

PIPE DISCHARGE(M^3/S)=? 0.5

ABRUPT ENTRANCE, K=1
------------------------------
DOWNSTREAM PIPE DIAMETER (M)=? 0.25
HEADLOSS (M)= 5.28812

ANY FURTHER FITTINGS ETC?  (Y/N)? Y
------------------------------
ABRUPT ENTRANCE (1)
ABRUPT EXIT (2)
SUDDEN ENLARGEMENT(3)
------------------------------

SELECT FITTING BY INPUTTING CODE NUMBER? 2

PIPE DISCHARGE(M^3/S)=? 0.5

ABRUPT EXIT, K=0.5
------------------------------
UPSTREAM PIPE DIAMETER (M)=? 0.25
HEADLOSS (M)= 2.64406

ANY FURTHER FITTINGS ETC?  (Y/N)? Y
------------------------------
ABRUPT ENTRANCE (1)
ABRUPT EXIT (2)
SUDDEN ENLARGEMENT(3)
------------------------------
```

Example 3.3 3RESPROB: solution by quantity balancing   59

```
SELECT FITTING BY INPUTTING CODE NUMBER? 3

PIPE DISCHARGE(M^3/S)=? 0.25

SUDDEN ENLARGEMENT, K=(1-(D1/D2)^2)
------------------------------------------------
UPSTREAM PIPE DIAMETER (M)=? 0.25
DOWNSTREAM DIAMETER (M)=? 0.5
HEADLOSS (M)= .991522

ANY FURTHER FITTINGS ETC?   (Y/N)? N

READY
```

Program notes

(1) At lines 40—60 the directory of fittings that can be analysed is held. This section can be extended to include as many as the operator desires. An index number is given to each fitment and is used to select the relevant segment of the program at lines 150—170.

(2) Since pipe discharge is required for head loss evaluation in all cases this is input next before the program moves to the particular section required.

(3) After head loss evaluation for a feature, the operator decides whether to continue by responding to the prompt at line 480. If a single branch pipe-line is being analysed then discharge at any section will be a constant and a return to the start of the new calculation may be speeded up by moving line 120 to before line 30 and perhaps going directly to line 90.

Example 3.3 3RESPROB: solution by quantity balancing

Three reservoirs are connected by three pipes which meet at a common junction as shown in Figure 3.8. The pipes leading from the three reservoirs 1, 2 and 3 have resistance coefficients (= $fL/3d^5$ where f is pipe friction factor, L is pipe length and d is pipe diameter) K1, K2

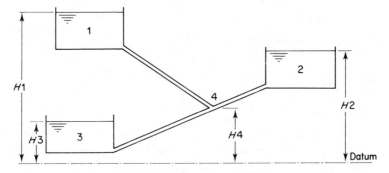

Figure 3.8 Three reservoir problem

and K3 of magnitude 2000, 2700 and 4200 s^2/m^5 respectively. The water level in the reservoirs is 60, 30 and 15 m above datum (represented in the figure by H1, H2 and H3 respectively). H4 is the height of junction 4 above datum.

Write a program to calculate the flow in each of the three pipes.

```
LIST


3RESPROB    3-JUL-81   14:32:39

10 PRINT "SOLUTION TO 3 RESERVOIR PROBLEM"
20 PRINT
30 DATA 2000,2700,4200,60,30,15
40 READ K1,K2,K3,H1,H2,H3
50 PRINT "INPUT ASSUMED HEAD AT JUNCTION 4 (M)    ";
60 INPUT H4
70 D1=H1-H4
80 D2=H2-H4
90 D3=H3-H4
100 Q1=SQR(ABS(D1)/K1)
110 Q2=SQR(ABS(D2)/K2)
120 Q3=SQR(ABS(D3)/K3)
130 Q=Q1-Q2-Q3
140 IF ABS(Q)<1.00000E-04 THEN 210
150 C=((Q1/ABS(D1))+(Q2/ABS(D2))+(Q3/ABS(D3)))/2
160 H=-Q/C
170 D1=D1+H
180 D2=D2+H
190 D3=D3+H
200 GO TO 100
210 PRINT
220 PRINT "Q1","Q2","Q3"
230 PRINT "M^3/S","M^3/S","M^3/S"
240 PRINT "_____"
250 PRINT Q1,Q2,Q3
260 END

READY


RUN


3RESPROB    3-JUL-81   14:33:10

SOLUTION TO 3 RESERVOIR PROBLEM

INPUT ASSUMED HEAD AT JUNCTION 4 (M)    ? 33

Q1              Q2              Q3
M^3/S           M^3/S           M^3/S
-------------------------------------------------
 .111869         .0429076        .0689563

READY
```

Program notes

(1) The data for the problem are input at line 30 and read at line 40.
(2) The problem is to be solved by the method known as quantity balancing. In this case a value of head is assumed at junction 4 and input as H4 at line 60. In lines 70–90 the head drop across the 3 pipes

Example 3.4 PIPENETWK: solution by head balancing   61

is evaluated (without attention to sign) and the resulting discharges evaluated at lines 100–120 as Q1, Q2 and Q3.

(3) A correct solution has been achieved if the inflow to junction 4 matches the outflow (i.e. at line 130, Q should be zero or, as expressed in line 140, very small).

(4) In lines 150–160 a correction to the assumed value of head at 4 is derived where a change in the value of H4 is found of the form

$$H = -\sum_{i=1}^{i=3} Q_i \bigg/ \sum_{i=1}^{i=3} \frac{Q_i}{2|D_i|} \qquad (3.28)$$

New values of head drop across the three pipes are now calculated and used to re-evaluate the out-of-balance discharge at junction 4.

(5) Results are printed, commencing at line 220.

Example 3.4 PIPENETWK: solution by head balancing

The distribution main shown in Figure 3.5 has the following characteristics

Pipe	Friction factor	Length (m)	Diameter (m)
1	0.01172	1000	0.25
2	0.00768	500	0.20
3	0.01308	1120	0.25
4	0.01172	1000	0.25
5	0.01152	500	0.20

At junction A, 0.06 m³/s flows in and there are outflows of 0.01, 0.02 and 0.03 m³/s at junctions B, C and D respectively.

It is required that the flow in each of the five pipes be evaluated using the method of head balancing.

Write a program using the head-balancing technique to evaluate the individual pipe discharges.

```
LIST

PIPENETWK   3-JUL-81   14:43:54

10 PRINT "PIPE NETWORK ANALYSIS"
20 PRINT
30 DATA 0.01172,1000,0.25,0.00768,500,.2
40 DATA 0.01308,1120,0.25,0.01172,1000,0.25
50 DATA 0.01152,500,0.2,0.01308,1120,0.25
60 DATA 0.03,0.02,-0.01,0.01,-0.02,0.01
70 DIM F(50),L(50),D(50),K(50),H(50),Q(50),P(10),R(10),B(10)
80 PRINT "PIPE NO","RES COEFF"
90 FOR I=1 TO 6
100 READ F(I),L(I),D(I)
110 K(I)=F(I)*L(I)/(3*D(I)^5)
120 PRINT I,K(I)
```

```
130 NEXT I
140 PRINT
150 PRINT
160 FOR I=1 TO 6
170 READ Q(I)
180 NEXT I
190 PRINT
200 PRINT "PIPE NO","HEAD DROP (M)"
210 FOR I=1 TO 6
220 H(I)=K(I)*Q(I)^2
230 PRINT I,H(I)
240 NEXT I
250 PRINT
260 PRINT "LOOP 123"
270 PRINT "H DROP SUM","H/Q SUM","CORRECN (M^3/S)"
280 P(1)=H(1)+H(2)-H(3)
290 R(1)=H(1)/Q(1)+H(2)/Q(2)-H(3)/Q(3)
300 B(1)=-P(1)/(2*R(1))
310 PRINT P(1),R(1),B(1)
320 PRINT "LOOP 645"
330 P(2)=H(6)+H(4)-H(5)
340 R(2)=H(6)/Q(6)+H(4)/Q(4)-H(5)/Q(5)
350 B(2)=-P(2)/(2*R(2))
360 PRINT P(2),R(2),B(2)
370 PRINT
380 REM FIND NEW DISCHARGES BY ADDING INCREMENTS. PIPE 3/6 HAS TWO!
390 Q(1)=Q(1)+B(1)
400 Q(2)=Q(2)+B(1)
410 Q(3)=Q(3)+B(1)-B(2)
420 Q(4)=Q(4)+B(2)
430 Q(5)=Q(5)+B(2)
440 Q(6)=Q(6)-B(1)+B(2)
450 PRINT "NEW DISCHARGES ARE"
460 PRINT Q(1),Q(2),Q(3)
470 PRINT Q(4),Q(5),Q(6)
480 PRINT
490 PRINT "DO YOU WISH TO GO ON? (Y/N)";
500 INPUT A$
510 IF A$="Y" THEN 190
520 END

READY




RUN


PIPENETWK  3-JUL-81  14:44:50

PIPE NETWORK ANALYSIS

PIPE NO        RES COEFF
  1            4000.43
  2            4000
  3            5000.4
  4            4000.43
  5            6000
  6            5000.4


PIPE NO        HEAD DROP (M)
  1            3.60038
  2            1.6
  3            .50004
  4            .400043
  5            2.4
  6            .50004
```

Example 3.4 PIPENETWK: solution by head balancing   63

```
LOOP 123
H DROP SUM      H/Q SUM       CORRECN (M^3/S)
 4.70035        250.017       -9.40006E-03
LOOP 645
-1.49992        210.008        3.57109E-03

NEW DISCHARGES ARE
 .0205999       .0105999      -.0229712
 .0135711      -.0164289       .0229712

DO YOU WISH TO GO ON? (Y/N)? Y

PIPE NO      HEAD DROP (M)
  1            1.69761
  2             .449435
  3            2.63858
  4             .736777
  5            1.61945
  6            2.63858


LOOP 123
H DROP SUM      H/Q SUM       CORRECN (M^3/S)
-.491532        239.673        1.02542E-03
LOOP 645
 1.7559         267.728       -3.27926E-03

NEW DISCHARGES ARE
 .0216254       .0116254      -.0186665
 .0102918      -.0197082       .0186665

DO YOU WISH TO GO ON? (Y/N)? Y

PIPE NO      HEAD DROP (M)
  1            1.87082
  2             .540596
  3            1.74232
  4             .423733
  5            2.33047
  6            1.74232

LOOP 123
H DROP SUM      H/Q SUM       CORRECN (M^3/S)
 .669096        226.352       -1.47800E-03
LOOP 645
-.164413        252.761        3.25236E-04

NEW DISCHARGES ARE
 .0201474       .0101474      -.0204697
 .0106171      -.0193829       .0204697

DO YOU WISH TO GO ON? (Y/N)? Y

PIPE NO      HEAD DROP (M)
  1            1.62384
  2             .411876
  3            2.09521
  4             .450937
  5            2.25419
  6            2.09521


LOOP 123
H DROP SUM      H/Q SUM       CORRECN (M^3/S)
-.0594976       223.544        1.33078E-04
LOOP 645
 .29196         261.127       -5.59039E-04

NEW DISCHARGES ARE
 .0202804       .0102804      -.0197776
 .010058       -.019942        .0197776

DO YOU WISH TO GO ON? (Y/N)? Y
```

```
PIPE NO      HEAD DROP (M)
  1              1.64536
  2               .42275
  3              1.95592
  4               .404699
  5              2.38609
  6              1.95592


LOOP 123
H DROP SUM    H/Q SUM        CORRECN (M^3/S)
 .112189      221.148        -2.53652E-04
LOOP 645
-.0254729     258.784         4.92165E-05


NEW DISCHARGES ARE
 .0200268     .0100268       -.0200805
 .0101073    -.0198928        .0200805


DO YOU WISH TO GO ON? (Y/N)? Y

PIPE NO      HEAD DROP (M)
  1              1.60446
  2               .402146
  3              2.01628
  4               .40867
  5              2.37433
  6              2.01628


LOOP 123
H DROP SUM    H/Q SUM        CORRECN (M^3/S)
-9.67884E-03  220.633         2.19342E-05
LOOP 645
 .0506246     260.2          -9.72801E-05


NEW DISCHARGES ARE
 .0200487     .0100487       -.0199612
 .01001      -.01999          .0199612


DO YOU WISH TO GO ON? (Y/N)? Y

PIPE NO      HEAD DROP (M)
  1              1.60798
  2               .403907
  3              1.99242
  4               .400841
  5              2.39761
  6              1.99242


LOOP 123
H DROP SUM    H/Q SUM        CORRECN (M^3/S)
 .0194685     220.212        -4.42040E-05
LOOP 645
-4.35281E-03  259.799         8.37728E-06


NEW DISCHARGES ARE
 .0200045     .0100045       -.0200138
 .0100183    -.0199817        .0200138


DO YOU WISH TO GO ON? (Y/N)? Y

PIPE NO      HEAD DROP (M)
  1              1.60089
  2               .400362
  3              2.00293
  4               .401512
  5              2.3956
  6              2.00293


LOOP 123
H DROP SUM    H/Q SUM        CORRECN (M^3/S)
-1.67060E-03  220.122         3.79472E-06
```

Example 3.4 PIPENETWK: solution by head balancing   65

```
LOOP 645
   8.83842E-03    260.045      -1.69940E-05

NEW DISCHARGES ARE
   .0200083       .0100083     -.019993
   .0100014      -.0199986      .019993

DO YOU WISH TO GO ON? (Y/N)? N

READY
```

Program notes

(1) The data for the pipes are input in lines 30–50 where it should be noted that the diagonal pipe labelled 3 and 6 in Figure 3.5 is included twice since it will appear in two loops of the network 123 and 645. At line 60 estimates of the discharges in the pipes are input, values being chosen such that at each junction the continuity equation is satisfied. The negative sign on the third value (−0.01) indicates that in pipe 3 the flow is in the opposite sense to that taken round the loop in which it occurs. Thus the value for pipe 6 is +0.01 because its flow direction is in the same sense as the loop direction.

(2) In the loop between lines 90 and 130, friction factors, lengths and diameters are read and the resistance coefficients for the (effectively) 6 pipes are calculated and printed.

(3) In lines 160 to 180 the assumed discharge values are read and in lines 210 to 240 the head drops across the pipes based on these assumed figures are found and printed.

(4) The essence of the head balancing technique is that the head drop between two points in a network should be the same no matter what route is taken between the two points. In this problem two loops of pipe 123 and 645 are considered, both starting and ending at junction A and therefore both having a net head drop of zero round each. In lines 280–300 the total head drop round loop 123 is evaluated as $P(1)$ where due regard is paid to sign. The algebraic sum of the H/Q values for each pipe is calculated as $R(1)$ and the correction to the assumed discharge is found as $B(1)$ where generally

$$B_{\text{loop}} = -\Sigma_{\text{loop}}H/2\Sigma_{\text{loop}}(H/Q) \qquad (3.29)$$

These values are printed and the same process repeated for loop 645.

(5) The new corrected discharges are now evaluated. The REM statement at line 380 indicates the calculation to be performed, noting that the common pipe attracts two corrections. These revised discharges are found in lines 390–440 and printed.

(6) The printed output can be inspected before any decision to proceed further with the calculation is taken. In the present problem results after only 5 iterations are probably acceptable, those achieved after 11 are more than adequate.

Example 3.5 SURGETANK: evaluation of levels on system closure

The surge tank shown in Figure 3.7 is circular in cross-section of 6 m diameter. The pipe leading from the reservoir is of length 3000 m, diameter 1 m and has a friction factor of 0.005. When the turbines are closed down by suddenly closing the valve the level in the surge tank begins to rise. Write a program to show how the level in the surge tank varies with time after valve closure if the initial velocity of water in the pipe is 3.0 m/s and all losses are purely frictional.

```
LIST


SURGETANK   3-JUL-81   14:55:08

10 PRINT "VARIATION OF WATER LEVEL IN A CYLINDRICAL SURGE TANK"
20 PRINT
30 DIM Y(50),V(50)
40 DATA 0.005,3000,3,1,6
50 READ F,L,C,D1,D2
60 T=2*PI*(D2/D1)*SQR(L/9.81)
70 PRINT "OSCILLATION PERIOD IN SECONDS IS   ";
80 PRINT T
90 PRINT
100 PRINT "SELECT SUITABLE TIME STEP (SECS)   ="；
110 INPUT S
120 PRINT "HOW MANY STEPS?    ";
130 INPUT N
140 PRINT
150 K1=4*F*L/(2*9.81*D1)
160 K2=(D1/D2)^2*S
170 K3=9.81*S/L
180 Y(0)=-4*F*L*C*C/(2*9.81*D1)
190 V(0)=C
200 PRINT "TIME","SURGE TANK","PIPE VEL","DEL Y","DEL V"
210 PRINT "SECS","LEVEL (M)","M/S","M","M/S"
220 PRINT "----------------------------------------------------"
230 A=K2*V(0)
240 B=0
250 PRINT 0,Y(0),V(0),A,B
260 FOR I=1 TO N
270 Y(I)=Y(I-1)+A
280 V(I)=V(I-1)+B
290 B=-K3*(Y(I)+K1*V(I)*ABS(V(I)))
300 A=K2*V(I)
310 R=I*S
320 PRINT R,Y(I),V(I),A,B
330 NEXT I
340 END

READY




RUN


SURGETANK   3-JUL-81   14:55:49

VARIATION OF WATER LEVEL IN A CYLINDRICAL SURGE TANK

OSCILLATION PERIOD IN SECONDS IS   659.261

SELECT SUITABLE TIME STEP (SECS)   =? 10
HOW MANY STEPS?    ? 40
```

Example 3.5 SURGETANK: evaluation of levels on system closure   67

TIME SECS	SURGE TANK LEVEL (M)	PIPE VEL M/S	DEL Y M	DEL V M/S
0	-27.5229	3	.833333	0
10	-26.6896	3	.833333	-.02725
20	-25.8563	2.97275	.825764	-.0382242
30	-25.0305	2.93453	.815146	-.0426466
40	-24.2154	2.89188	.8033	-.0444542
50	-23.4121	2.84743	.790951	-.0452085
60	-22.6211	2.80222	.778394	-.0455314
70	-21.8427	2.75669	.765746	-.0456743
80	-21.077	2.71101	.753059	-.0457409
90	-20.3239	2.66527	.740353	-.0457744
100	-19.5836	2.6195	.727638	-.0457932
110	-18.8559	2.5737	.714917	-.0458056
120	-18.141	2.5279	.702194	-.0458152
130	-17.4388	2.48208	.689467	-.0458236
140	-16.7493	2.43626	.676738	-.0458316
150	-16.0726	2.39043	.664007	-.0458394
160	-15.4086	2.34459	.651274	-.0458475
170	-14.7573	2.29874	.638539	-.0458557
180	-14.1188	2.25288	.625801	-.0458641
190	-13.493	2.20702	.613061	-.0458729
200	-12.8799	2.16115	.600318	-.0458819
210	-12.2796	2.11526	.587573	-.0458913
220	-11.692	2.06937	.574826	-.0459011
230	-11.1172	2.02347	.562076	-.0459113
240	-10.5551	1.97756	.549322	-.0459219
250	-10.0058	1.93164	.536566	-.0459329
260	-9.46924	1.88571	.523807	-.0459445
270	-8.94543	1.83976	.511045	-.0459565
280	-8.43439	1.7938	.498279	-.0459691
290	-7.93611	1.74784	.48551	-.0459822
300	-7.4506	1.70185	.472737	-.045996
310	-6.97786	1.65586	.45996	-.0460104
320	-6.5179	1.60985	.44718	-.0460254
330	-6.07072	1.56382	.434395	-.0460413
340	-5.63633	1.51778	.421606	-.0460579
350	-5.21472	1.47172	.408812	-.0460754
360	-4.80591	1.42565	.396013	-.0460938
370	-4.4099	1.37955	.383209	-.0461132
380	-4.02669	1.33344	.3704	-.0461336
390	-3.65629	1.28731	.357585	-.0461553
400	-3.2987	1.24115	.344764	-.0461782

READY

RUN

SURGETANK   3-JUL-81   14:58:00

VARIATION OF WATER LEVEL IN A CYLINDRICAL SURGE TANK

OSCILLATION PERIOD IN SECONDS IS   659.261

SELECT SUITABLE TIME STEP (SECS) =? 50
HOW MANY STEPS?   ? 40

TIME SECS	SURGE TANK LEVEL (M)	PIPE VEL M/S	DEL Y M	DEL V M/S
0	-27.5229	3	4.16667	0
50	-23.3563	3	4.16667	-.68125
100	-19.1896	2.31875	3.22049	.449199
150	-15.9691	2.76795	3.84437	-1.21982
200	-12.1247	1.54813	2.15018	.784046
250	-9.97457	2.33217	3.23913	-1.08868
300	-6.73544	1.2435	1.72708	.3281
350	-5.00836	1.5716	2.18278	-.416094

400	-2.82558	1.1555	1.60487	-.205612
450	-1.22071	.949892	1.31929	-.25156
500	.0985801	.698331	.969905	-.259951
550	1.06848	.43838	.608861	-.270786
600	1.67735	.167594	.23277	-.28829
650	1.91012	-.120696	-.167633	-.30502
700	1.74248	-.425716	-.591272	-.194279
750	1.15121	-.619995	-.861104	3.97385E-03
800	.290107	-.616021	-.855585	.142308
850	-.565478	-.473713	-.657934	.204657
900	-1.22341	-.269055	-.373688	.236223
950	-1.5971	-.0328319	-.0455999	.261665
1000	-1.6427	.228833	.317823	.242399
1050	-1.32488	.471232	.654489	.105587
1100	-.670387	.576819	.801138	-.056752
1150	.130751	.520067	.722316	-.156613
1200	.853067	.363455	.504798	-.205526
1250	1.35787	.157929	.219345	-.234482
1300	1.57721	-.0765531	-.106324	-.254944
1350	1.47089	-.331497	-.460412	-.185545
1400	1.01047	-.517042	-.718113	-.0315465
1450	.292361	-.548588	-.761928	.102673
1500	-.469567	-.445915	-.619326	.176194
1550	-1.08889	-.269721	-.374612	.214409
1600	-1.46351	-.0553119	-.0768221	.240813
1650	-1.54033	.185501	.25764	.234638
1700	-1.28269	.420139	.583526	.121461
1750	-.69916	.5416	.752222	-.0323525
1800	.0530618	.509247	.707288	-.138342
1850	.76035	.370905	.515146	-.193103
1900	1.2755	.177803	.246948	-.224351
1950	1.52244	-.0465478	-.0646498	-.247836
2000	1.45779	-.294384	-.408867	-.195018

READY

Program notes

(1) Data for the problem are input at line 40 and read at line 50 where F, L, C, D1 and D2 are friction factor, pipe length, initial velocity, pipe diameter and surge tank diameter respectively. The data are used to calculate the oscillation period of the system as T which is then printed.

(2) Inspection of this output determines the response to the prompts at lines 100 and 120 which sets the incremental time between calculation and the number of such calculations.

(3) Equations (3.26) and (3.27) are to be solved and they should first be written in terms of increments and rearranged to give

$$\Delta v = -(y + Kv|v|)\, g\Delta t/L \qquad (3.30)$$

and

$$\Delta y = a\Delta t v/A \qquad (3.31)$$

In the program K1 = K (= $4fL/2gd$), K2 = $a\Delta t/A$ and K3 = $g\Delta t/L$.

(4) The solution is initiated at lines 180 and 190 where the operating level of the surge tank is evaluated. This will be below the reservoir level by an amount equal to the frictional head loss in the pipe. The initial fluid velocity is set at 3 m/s and the surge tank level, pipe velocity,

change in level, A, and change in velocity, B that occur in the first time-step are printed at line 250.

(5) In the loop between lines 260 and 330 the most recent values of y and v are used to calculate the change in v during that time-step and this is used to update the flow velocity enabling the surge tank level to be evaluated and so on, till the full number of time steps has been taken. Results are printed at line 320.

(6) Depending on the length of time step a more or less accurate assessment of the actual level variation will be obtained. The first set of output is for a short time-step (compared with the oscillation perod) of 10 seconds. The second set of results for a time-step of 50 seconds clearly shows the decaying amplitude oscillation of the tank level though the accuracy of the output values will be diminished.

PROBLEMS

(3.1) In an experiment to investigate the occurrence of laminar and turbulent flow in a pipe a small-bore, smooth pipe carrying water was employed. The internal diameter of the pipe was 3 mm and the length between pressure tappings was 1050 mm. The rate of flow down the pipe was varied and the pressure drop at the two measuring stations was recorded on a mercury—water manometer for high flow-rates, and on a water-filled manometer when the mercury manometer sensitivity became too small at low flow-rates. The volume flow was measured by recording the time taken to collect a known volume of water. Measurements over the entire discharge range were as shown below

Mercury manometer

h_1 (mm)	h_2 (mm)	Volume collected (1)	Time (s)
1000	22	0.905	30
713	135	0.670	30
568	206	0.768	45
420	258	0.685	60
386	272	0.590	60
359	281	0.493	60

Water manometer

h_1 (mm)	h_2 (mm)	Volume collected (1)	Time (s)
751	123	0.378	60
560	166	0.312	60
470	210	0.210	60
394	248	0.210	60
340	274	0.053	60

h_1 is the reading on the manometer at the pipe inlet end while h_2 is the reading near pipe outlet.

Write a program to analyse these data to calculate the friction factor in the pipe for each of the flows together with the corresponding Reynolds number.

The friction factor may be calculated by using the Darcy—Weisbach Equation (3.3). The Reynolds number should be based on the pipe diameter as the characteristic length. The dynamic viscosity of water at the temperature of the experiment may be taken as 1.31×10^{-3} Nsm^{-2}. The program should also evaluate and tabulate log f and log Re so that a graph of the results may be constructed. Ideally the program should be capable of analysing data from other similar experiments using different fluids in different diameter pipes.

(3.2) It is often required that the friction factor for a rough pipe be evaluated when, for example, a pump system is being matched with a pipe network. In such a case the flow rate and fluid heads in the system will be required and this often involves making adjustments to the initial calculations in the light of later results. Such a process is illustrated in Example 5.3 where the adjustment of the friction factor used in the calculation is adjusted manually.

Write a simple program that can be used to evaluate friction factor from Moody's Equation (3.14) for given values of roughness ratio k/d and Reynolds number that could, without too much difficulty, be incorporated in a problem such as that mentioned above.

(3.3) A pipe made of cast iron of internal roughness 0.25 mm is to carry a discharge of 0.15 m^3/s and is laid at a slope, S_f, of 1 in 450. Write a program to determine the size of the pipe required using the Colebrooke—White formula (Equation (3.15)) and the Darcy—Weisbach Equation (3.3) where, if uniform flow in the pipe is assumed, the slope S_f may be equated to the head drop per unit length of pipe h_f/L.

The main step in the program should be to combine the two equations, eliminating friction factor between them and then solving the resultant equation iteratively to obtain the required diameter of pipe. As a final stage in the program the nature of the flow should be established (i.e. laminar, transitional, turbulent) by evaluating the flow Reynolds number.

(3.4) Example 3.2 is a directory of local head losses in a pipe-line whereby the pressure drop associated with a particular feature of a system is evaluated. It would be useful to be able to work along a pipe-line containing different features and fittings, etc. from entrance to exit summing up the local head losses as expressed by Equation (3.16) and the frictional head losses as given by the Darcy—Weisbach Equation (3.3).

By drawing on the elements presented in the program of Example

3.2 and adding further features if necessary, write a program capable of summing all the losses in a typical pipe-line carrying water, using the system illustrated in Figure 3.4 for which the following data apply

Feature		Geometry, etc.
C	sharp entry	From reservoir to pipe of diameter 0.1 m
D	smooth pipe	Diameter 0.1 m, length 3 m
E	pump entry	Diameter 0.1 m, equivalent length 1.5 m
P	pump	Pump head 20 m
F	smooth pipe	Diameter 0.1 m, length 4 m
G	sudden expansion	Diameter 0.1 m to 0.15 m
H	smooth pipe	Diameter 0.15 m, length 5 m
I	abrupt exit	Diameter 0.15 m to reservoir

The discharge from the system is 0.2 m³/s.

(3.5) By adopting an approach similar to that employed in Example 3.4, determine the flows in the pipes of the network shown in Figure

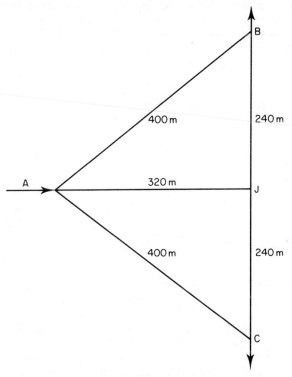

Figure 3.9 Pipe network for Problem (3.5)

3.9 if the inflow at A is 3.8 m^3/s and the outflows to atmosphere at B and C are 1.4 m^3/s and 2.20 m^3/s respectively. All the pipes are of 400 mm diameter and the friction factor for them all may be taken as 0.0045.

(3.6) The universal velocity distribution law, Equation (3.9) and the laminar sub-layer Equation (3.10) when plotted, intersect at a certain value of the parameter $yv*/\nu$ corresponding to a particular distance from the pipe wall in a given flow. Write a program to determine the value of the parameters $v/v*$ and $yv*/\nu$ at this intersection point.

If a pipe may be considered hydraulically smooth if any wall roughness is submerged in the laminar sublayer, determine the maximum permissible height of such roughness to maintain a smooth configuration for a pipe of 0.1 m diameter carrying a discharge of 3.5 10^{-2} m^3/s of water if there is a pressure drop of 0.02 bar per metre of pipe. The dynamic viscosity of water may be taken as 1.2 10^{-3} Ns/m^2.

(3.7) Write a program that can be used to calculate the speed of a shock wave that will be generated in an elastic pipe when a valve at the end of the pipe-line is suddenly closed. The program should also be used to calculate the pressure rise that will accompany the valve closure and the stress produced in the material of the pipe. This is known as the hoop stress σ_h and for a pipe with an internal pressure p the hoop stress is given by

$$\sigma_h = pr/t \qquad (3.32)$$

where r is pipe radius and t is pipe wall thickness. Information on several different pipes made from different materials is given below

Material	Young's modulus (N/m^2)	Wall thickness (m)	Internal diameter (m)
Steel	210 10^9	0.01	0.09
Steel	210 10^9	0.02	0.08
Copper	124 10^9	0.003	0.075
Aluminium	70 10^9	0.01	0.09
Glass	50 10^9	0.005	0.025
Polythene	0.5 10^9	0.01	0.09
Concrete	15 10^9	0.10	0.90

The discharge in each pipe may be taken as 0.1 m^3/s, with the exception of the concrete pipe where the flow is 1 m^3/s.

Equation (3.20) should be used to evaluate water hammer wave speeds. The bulk modulus of water may be taken as 2.10^9 N/m^2.

(3.8) A steel pipe-line of diameter 1 m carries a discharge of 2 m^3/s from a reservoir under a head of 440 m. Write a program to calculate the thickness of the walls of the pipe if it is to be able to withstand the rise in head caused by the instantaneous closure of a valve at the outlet of the pipe. The program should also be used to calculate the pressure rise at the valve. It may be assumed that the safe stress in the steel (the hoop stress given by Equation (3.32)) is 120 N/mm². Young's modulus for steel is 210 kN/mm² and the bulk modulus of water is 2 kN/mm².

The maximum permissible pressure can be calculated from Equation (3.32) and hence, by considering the steady flow head at the valve, an expression for the limit of the pressure rise may be derived as a function of wall thickness. Then, by solving this equation simultaneously with Equation (3.20) iteratively, the required wall thickness will be obtained.

(3.9) When a valve at the end of a pipe-line is closed in a time longer than a pipe period, the velocity of flow in the pipe is given by Equation (3.23). This equation can be combined with Equation (3.17) expressed in terms of head as

$$H - H_R = -\frac{L}{g} \frac{dv}{dt} \tag{3.33}$$

to yield an equation for the variation of head behind the valve with time of the form

$$\frac{dH}{dt} = \frac{2\left[\dfrac{(H_R - H)g}{L V_0} \sqrt{\left(\dfrac{H_R}{H}\right)} + \dfrac{1}{T} \right] H}{1 - t/T} \tag{3.34}$$

where the notation is as in the text.

Write a program to show how the head behind the valve varies with time. This may be accomplished by splitting the valve closure time T into n increments dt ($= T/n$) and using Equation (3.34) to evaluate the initial head change in the first time-step. Then using this value the head at the end of one time-step can be calculated as

$$H_{dt} = H_R + \frac{dH}{dt}\bigg|_0 dt \tag{3.35}$$

and this value of H used to evaluate the change in head in the next increment of time and so on. Great care must be taken over the problem of reflections at the end of the pipe away from the valve and the effect such reflections will have on the total head predicted at the valve.

The program should attempt to incorporate a system whereby such effects can be accommodated.

Take as an example a pipe-line 3 km long leading from a reservoir. When the valve fitted at the downstream end is open, the head just upstream of the valve is 200 m and the water velocity is 5 m/s. The valve closes in 40 s and it may be assumed that velocity variation in the pipe is given by Equation (3.23). To simplify solution of the head variation evaluate the head change in a period of time less than a pipe period before attempting to consider the problem of reflections noted above.

(3.10) When a valve is suddenly opened at the end of a long pipe-line there is a time-lag before uniform flow conditions are established. Equation (3.33) may be rewritten and integrated to yield an equation relating the pipe velocity v, at time t of the form

$$t = \frac{L}{\sqrt{(2gH_RK)}} \; \ln \left[\frac{\sqrt{\dfrac{2gH_R}{K}} + v}{\sqrt{\dfrac{2gH_R}{K}} - v} \right] \qquad (3.36)$$

where K is as in Equation (3.16).

Assuming that losses are purely frictional, write a program to show the variation of velocity with time in the pipe-line of Problem (3.9) given that the pipe is of diameter 0.15 m and has a friction factor of 0.005.

Chapter 4
Flow in open channels

ESSENTIAL THEORY

4.1 Introduction

The flow that occurs in open channels differs from pipe-flow in that, whereas pressure varies from point to point in the flow direction in a pipe, the free surface pressure in a channel has a constant value, usually atmospheric. Also, since cross-sectional area of flow in a channel is not determined by fixed boundaries, flow depth can vary from section to section without restraint. Flow depth can also vary with time. Based on these ideas, channel flow can be categorised as either steady flow in

STEADY FLOW		
Type	Example	Comment
Uniform	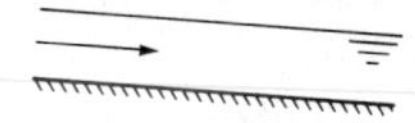	Constant depth at all times
Gradually varied	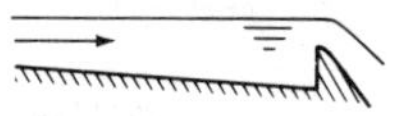	Behind weir depth varies slowly with distance
Rapidly varied	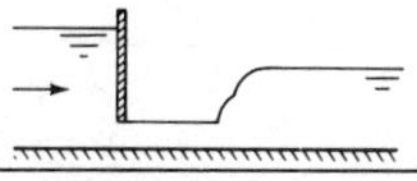	Hydraulic jump causes sudden depth change in a short distance
UNSTEADY FLOW		
Uniform	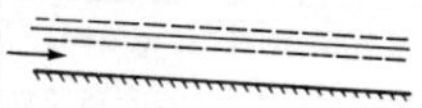	Depth varies suddenly from time to time (very rare)
Gradually varied	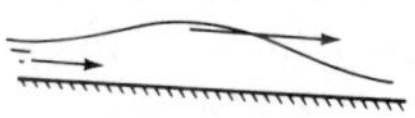	Long flood wave
Rapidly varied	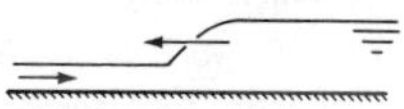	Short surge wave (e.g. tidal bore)

Figure 4.1 Flow classification

which flow depth does not change with time, or unsteady flow where depth is time-dependent. Six different flow regimes can be identified within this framework as set out in Figure 4.1.

4.2 Uniform flow

If the Colebrook–White expression for friction factor in rough pipe flow (Equation (3.15)) is modified by replacing pipe diameter, d, with hydraulic radius, R, and noting that for a circular conduit running full $R = d/4$ then Equation (4.1) results

$$1/\sqrt{f} = -2 \log_{10}\left(k/14.8R + 0.627/\text{Re}\sqrt{f}\right) \qquad (4.1)$$

where k is channel mean roughness height and Re is Reynolds number based on hydraulic radius. By combining this equation with the Darcy–Weisbach formula for channel friction factor

$$f = 8RSg/V^2 \qquad (4.2)$$

where V is mean channel flow velocity and S is channel bed slope then

$$V = -\sqrt{(32RSg)}\log_{10}\left(k/14.8R + 0.627V/\text{Re}\sqrt{8RSg}\right) \qquad (4.3)$$

It is usual to omit the second term in the logarithm in the case of fully developed flow, when it can be shown to be much smaller than the first term.

Uniform flow velocity can also be described by means of the empirically based Manning formula where

$$V = \frac{R^{2/3}\,S^{1/2}}{n} \qquad (4.4)$$

in which n is the Manning roughness coefficient, a factor dependent mainly on surface roughness.

If a channel of given geometry is required to carry a certain discharge Q then modified forms of Equations (4.3) or (4.4) can be solved to evaluate the flow depth known as the normal depth y_n.

Summarising possible depths and discharges in a channel of given geometry is sometimes desirable and this can be accomplished by means of proportional depth charts relating depths and discharges normalised with respect to some reference value. The development of such a plot for a circular conduit is given in the program illustrated on p. 93 (Example 4.5).

In channel design it is important that the solution is both workable and efficient. For instance, in the case of a trapezoidal channel of base width b, side slope α and water depth y, since discharge will be maximised when hydraulic radius is a maximum, then it can be shown that for maximum discharge at fixed cross-sectional area A then

$$A = 2y^2 \cosec \alpha - y^2 \cot \alpha \qquad (4.5)$$

For maximum efficiency the hydraulic radius becomes $y/2$. If side slope can be varied then the 'best' section is one which has a slope of $60°$. 'Best' trapezoidal and rectangular sections are shown in Figure 4.2.

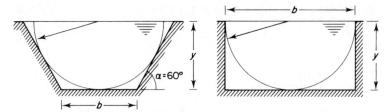

Figure 4.2 Best hydraulic sections

4.3 Gradually varied flow

The general case of gradually varied flow where characteristics exhibit only small changes over quite large reaches of channel is illustrated in Figure 4.3.

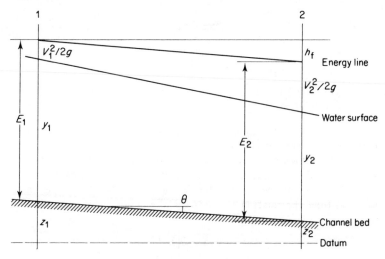

Figure 4.3 Gradually varied flow

Assuming minimal friction loss ($h_f = 0$) then the Bernoulli energy equation between sections 1 and 2 may be written

$$z_1 + y_1 + V_1{}^2/2g = z_2 + y_2 + V_2{}^2/2g = \begin{array}{c}\text{Constant}\\ \text{total}\\ \text{head}\end{array} \qquad (4.6)$$

It is often useful to measure energy relative to the channel base where $z = 0$ and then specific energy, E, is given by

$$E = y + V^2/2g \qquad (4.7)$$

For a given discharge, depth varies with specific energy as shown in Figure 4.4(a), while for a given specific energy, discharge varies with depth as in Figure 4.4(b).

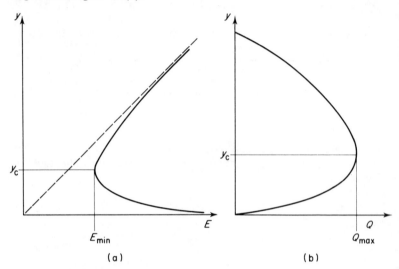

Figure 4.4(a) Variation of specific energy with depth (b) Variation of discharge with depth

The depth at minimum energy and maximum discharge is the critical depth y_c and the flow Froude number at this depth is unity. Froude number is defined as $V/\sqrt{gD}$ where V is the mean flow velocity and D is hydraulic depth defined as cross-sectional area divided by top width of water free surface. When the distance between sections is small, say Δx, then the relationship between the depth change and distance is

$$\Delta y/\Delta x = (S - S_f)/(1 - \mathrm{Fr}^2) \qquad (4.8)$$

where S_f is the friction slope (slope of energy line) and Fr is the average Froude number value between stations. This equation can be expressed in energy change terms as

$$\Delta x = \Delta E/(S - S_f) \qquad (4.9)$$

Depending on the magnitude and sign of the quantities of Equation

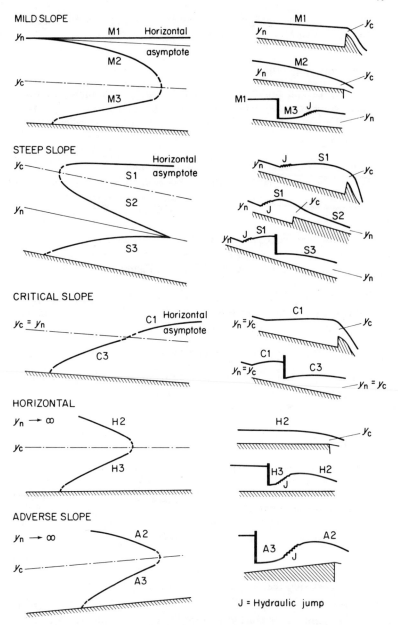

Figure 4.5 Flow profile classification [after Massey, *Mechanics of Fluids* 3rd ed., Van Nostrand Reinhold, (1975)]

(4.8) various surface profile shapes can be identified as summarised in Figure 4.5.

4.4 Rapidly varied flow

Surface profiles in non-uniform channel flow are determined by what happens at particular stations upstream and downstream of a given profile. Stations which fix the nature of the profile are called control sections and can be

(1) a control structure, e.g. weir, sluice, flume,
(2) a bed-slope change causing sub-critical flow to become super-critical,
(3) flow into or out of a static body of water, e.g. reservoir.

The flow associated with control type (1) may be termed rapidly varied flow. The governing equations for common hydraulic control structures are noted below with reference to Figure 4.6.

(a) A sluice-gate or undershot weir often causes a hydraulic jump downstream of the structure. The ratio of depths across the jump in a rectangular channel is given by

$$y_2/y_1 = \frac{1}{2} \left[\sqrt{(1 + 8\mathrm{Fr}_1^2)} - 1 \right] \qquad (4.10)$$

where Fr_1 is the Froude number upstream of the jump. Hydraulic jumps are also associated with other structures.

(b) A plate weir or notch is used as a measuring structure. The theoretical discharge over a rectangular notch is

$$Q = \frac{2}{3} B \sqrt{(2g)} H^{3/2} \qquad (4.11)$$

For a symmetrical V-notch of angle θ, discharge is

$$Q = \frac{8}{15} \sqrt{(2g)} \tan \frac{\theta}{2} H^{5/2} \qquad (4.12)$$

(c) The discharge over a broad-crested weir on which the flow depth is critical is given approximately by

$$Q = b \sqrt{g} \left(\frac{2}{3} E \right)^{3/2} \qquad (4.13)$$

If the approach velocity is ignored this can be written as

$$Q = 1.705 \, bH^{3/2} \qquad (4.14)$$

(d) A flume can operate as a venturi or drowned flume in which

$$Q = b_2 y_2 \sqrt{\left[\frac{2gh}{1 + (b_2 y_2 / b_1 y_1)^2} \right]} \qquad (4.15)$$

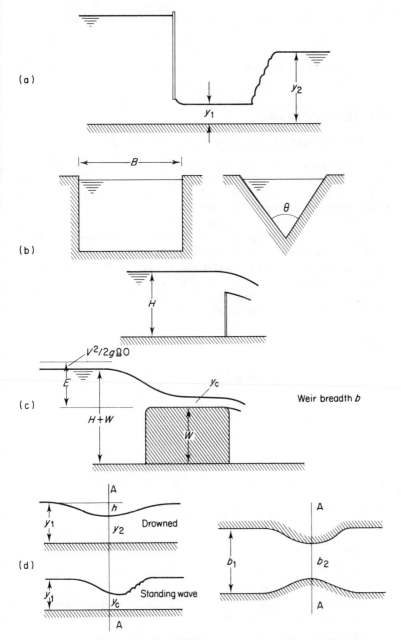

Figure 4.6(a) Flow under a sluice-gate (*b*) Plate weirs (*c*) Broad-crested weir (*d*) Flow through flumes

or as a standing wave flume where (similarly to Equation (4.13))

$$Q = 1.705 \, b_2 y_1^{3/2} \qquad (4.16)$$

The analysis of unsteady channel flow is beyond the scope of this present work.

WORKED EXAMPLES

Example 4.1 CHANDESN: design of irrigation channel

A straight channel is to be designed to carry a maximum discharge of 10 m³/s between two points on an irrigation network 5 km apart and 179 m and 173 m above datum respectively. The channel is to be trapezoidal and, because local soil conditions are relatively unstable, the side slope is to be as shallow as possible. Also, because the space between areas under cultivation is limited, the channel top width should not be in excess of 4.5 m. If the material of the channel base and sides can be taken as having a mean roughness height of 15 mm, design a suitable section to carry this discharge.

In order to simplify design calculations the channel bottom width is to be set at twice the flow depth.

```
READY
LIST

CHANDESN    3-JUL-81   15:15:34

10 PRINT "CHANNEL DESIGN"
20 PRINT
30 PRINT "DESIGN DISCHARGE (CUMECS)      ";
40 INPUT Q
50 PRINT "CHANNEL ROUGHNESS (M)      ";
60 INPUT K
70 PRINT "CHANNEL SLOPE      ";
80 INPUT S
90 PRINT "TOP WIDTH LIMIT (M)      ";
100 INPUT C
110 PRINT "RATIO BASE/DEPTH      ";
120 INPUT N
130 PRINT
140 PRINT "SIDE-SLOPE ANGLE (DEG)      ";
150 INPUT T
160 B=T*PI/180
170 PRINT "DEPTH (M)      ";
180 INPUT Y
185 PRINT
190 A=Y*Y*(N+1/(SIN(B)/COS(B)))
200 P=Y*(N+2/SIN(B))
210 R=A/P
220 Q1=-A*SQR(32*9.81*R*S)*LOG10(K/(14.8*R))
225 PRINT "----------------------------------------------------------"
230 PRINT "CALCULATED DISCHARGE      ",Q1
235 PRINT "----------------------------------------------------------"
240 D=Q-Q1
250 PRINT "DIFFERENCE BETWEEN Q AND Q1",D
255 PRINT
```

Example 4.1 CHANDESN: design of irrigation channel   83

```
260 PRINT "IF D>0 INCREASE Y, IF D<-0.25 DECREASE Y"
265 PRINT
270 IF D>0 THEN 170
280 IF D<-.25 THEN 170
290 C1=(N*Y)+(2*Y)/(SIN(B)/COS(B))
300 IF C1>C THEN 140
310 W=N*Y
315 PRINT
320 PRINT "THETA","BASE","DEPTH","TOP"
325 PRINT "------------------------------------------------------------------"
330 PRINT T,W,Y,C1
335 PRINT
340 PRINT "DO YOU WANT TO TRY ANOTHER VALUE OF THETA? (Y OR N)";
350 INPUT A$
355 PRINT
360 IF A$="Y" THEN 140
370 END

READY


RUN

CHANDESN   3-JUL-81  15:16:29

CHANNEL DESIGN

DESIGN DISCHARGE (CUMECS)     ? 10
CHANNEL ROUGHNESS (M)     ? 0.015
CHANNEL SLOPE     ? 0.0012
TOP WIDTH LIMIT (M)     ? 4.5
RATIO BASE/DEPTH     ? 2

SIDE-SLOPE ANGLE (DEG)     ? 75
DEPTH (M)     ? 1.5

-----------------------------------------------------------------
CALCULATED DISCHARGE          8.34978
-----------------------------------------------------------------
DIFFERENCE BETWEEN Q AND Q1  1.65022

IF D>0 INCREASE Y, IF D<-0.25 DECREASE Y

DEPTH (M)     ? 1.8

-----------------------------------------------------------------
CALCULATED DISCHARGE          13.5289
-----------------------------------------------------------------
DIFFERENCE BETWEEN Q AND Q1  -3.52891

IF D>0 INCREASE Y, IF D<-0.25 DECREASE Y

DEPTH (M)     ? 1.62

-----------------------------------------------------------------
CALCULATED DISCHARGE          10.2373
-----------------------------------------------------------------
DIFFERENCE BETWEEN Q AND Q1  -.237258

IF D>0 INCREASE Y, IF D<-0.25 DECREASE Y

THETA        BASE        DEPTH        TOP
-----------------------------------------------------------------
  75          3.24        1.62         4.10815

DO YOU WANT TO TRY ANOTHER VALUE OF THETA? (Y OR N)? Y

SIDE-SLOPE ANGLE (DEG)     ? 66
DEPTH (M)     ? 1.55
```

```
-----------------------------------------------------------------------
CALCULATED DISCHARGE            10.1196
-----------------------------------------------------------------------
DIFFERENCE BETWEEN Q AND Q1 -.119563

IF D>0 INCREASE Y, IF D<-0.25 DECREASE Y


THETA           BASE            DEPTH           TOP
-----------------------------------------------------------------------
 66             3.1             1.55            4.48021

DO YOU WANT TO TRY ANOTHER VALUE OF THETA? (Y OR N)? N
```

Program notes

(1) Since material roughness is given as a mean roughness height k, then the Colebrooke–White Equation (4.3) can be used. Assuming fully developed turbulent flow, this can be simplified to give

$$V = -\sqrt{32RSg} \, \log_{10} (k/14.8R) \qquad (4.17)$$

There are many ways of approaching this problem which is essentially one of solving the above equation with due regard to geometrical and flow considerations.

(2) In response to the prompts between lines 30 and 110 the parameters that define the problem are input. These are design discharge, channel roughness and slope, the limit to the top width and the ratio of the base width to depth as Q, K, S, C and N respectively. There remains to be selected only values of the side-slope of the channel and an initial estimate of the depth of flow, input as T and Y. At line 160 the side slope input in degrees is converted to radians as B.

(3) In lines 190–210 the channel geometry for these inputs is calculated: cross-section area, wetted perimeter and hydraulic radius are evaluated as A, P and R. Then, using these quantities, the discharge for this geometry is evaluated as Q1 and printed at line 230. The difference between the actual and design discharge is found as D and printed at line 250. This output is examined by the operator in response to the comment printed at line 260 and, if the difference is large (>0.25 m³/s) the program returns to line 170 for adjustment of flow depth.

(4) If the difference is within the limit then for the present depth the corresponding value of top width is found at line 290 as Cl. If this value is greater than the maximum, the program returns to line 140 for the input of an adjusted side slope angle. If the top width is satisfactory then the channel base width is evaluated as W and, after suitable headings are printed at line 320, the side slope, base width, flow depth and top width are printed.

(5) If the solution is not yet considered the best, then the program offers the chance of further adjustment following the response to the

Example 4.2 GVFPROFIL: evaluation of backwater curve   85

prompt at line 340. The output shows, firstly a satisfactory solution incorporating quite steeply sloping sides, while the second represents the limiting case with regard to top width, etc.

Example 4.2 GVFPROFIL: evaluation of backwater curve

A trapezoidal channel has the dimensions shown in Figure 4.7. It is of longitudinal slope 0.0016, has a Manning n-value of 0.025 and carries a discharge of 11.35 m^3/s. Under such conditions the normal depth of flow is 1.025 m and the critical depth is 0.656 m. A weir is built across the channel such that the water backs up to a depth of 1.52 m immediately behind the structure. Compute how the depth of water varies with distance upstream of the dam to where the depth is 1% greater than the normal depth.

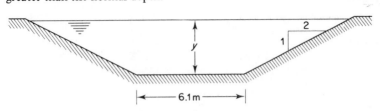

Figure 4.7 Channel cross-section for Example 4.2

```
LIST


GVFPROFIL   3-JUL-81   15:24:22

10 PRINT "FLOW PROFILE EVALUATION"
20 PRINT
30 DATA 1.52,1.03,6.1,11.35,.025,.0016,2
40 PRINT "STEP LENGTH (M)=      ";
50 INPUT Z
60 DIM X(100),E(100),F(100)
70 I=1
80 X(1)=0
90 READ Y1,Y0,B,Q,N,S,G
100 PRINT "DEPTH OF WATER      ","DISTANCE FROM WEIR    "
110 PRINT "METRES              ","METRES               "
120 PRINT Y1,,0
130 FOR Y=Y1 TO YO STEP Z
140 A=B*Y+G*Y^2
150 P=B+2*Y*SQR(1+G^2)
160 R=A/P
170 V=Q/A
180 E(I)=Y+V^2/(2*9.81)
190 F(I)=((V*N)/(R^(2/3)))^2
200 IF I=1 THEN 240
210 D=(E(I-1)-E(I))/(S-(F(I-1)+F(I))/2)
220 X(I)=X(I-1)+D
230 PRINT Y,,X(I)
240 I=I+1
250 NEXT Y
260 END

READY
```

```
RUN

GVFPROFIL  3-JUL-81  15:24:52

FLOW PROFILE EVALUATION

STEP LENGTH (M)=      ? -0.05
DEPTH OF WATER                  DISTANCE FROM WEIR
METRES                          METRES
 1.52                            0
 1.47                            39.126
 1.42                            79.7701
 1.37                            122.395
 1.32                            167.688
 1.27                            216.723
 1.22                            271.325
 1.17                            334.954
 1.12                            415.476
 1.07                            538.059

READY

RUN

GVFPROFIL  3-JUL-81  15:25:19

FLOW PROFILE EVALUATION

STEP LENGTH (M)=      ? -0.02
DEPTH OF WATER                  DISTANCE FROM WEIR
METRES                          METRES
 1.52                            0
 1.5                             15.4863
 1.48                            31.1806
 1.46                            47.1039
 1.44                            63.2808
 1.42                            79.7391
 1.4                             96.5113
 1.38                            113.635
 1.36                            131.156
 1.34                            149.126
 1.32                            167.609
 1.3                             186.682
 1.28                            206.441
 1.26                            227.003
 1.24                            248.519
 1.22                            271.183
 1.2                             295.254
 1.18                            321.083
 1.16                            349.172
 1.14                            380.26
 1.12                            415.514
 1.1                             456.93
 1.08                            508.362
 1.06                            578.865
 1.04                            699.687

READY

RUN

GVFPROFIL  3-JUL-81  15:26:09

FLOW PROFILE EVALUATION

STEP LENGTH (M)=      ? -0.01
DEPTH OF WATER                  DISTANCE FROM WEIR
METRES                          METRES
 1.52                            0
 1.51                            7.71807
```

Example 4.2 GVFPROFIL: evaluation of backwater curve   87

1.5	15.4855
1.49	23.3051
1.48	31.179
1.47	39.1102
1.46	47.1015
1.45	55.1561
1.44	63.2774
1.43	71.469
1.42	79.7346
1.41	88.0787
1.4	96.5057
1.39	105.021
1.38	113.629
1.37	122.336
1.36	131.148
1.35	140.072
1.34	149.116
1.33	158.288
1.32	167.598
1.31	177.054
1.3	186.669
1.29	196.455
1.28	206.426
1.27	216.597
1.26	226.986
1.25	237.613
1.24	248.5
1.23	259.674
1.22	271.163
1.21	283.002
1.2	295.232
1.19	307.9
1.18	321.062
1.17	334.786
1.16	349.153
1.15	364.266
1.14	380.249
1.13	397.265
1.12	415.524
1.11	435.304
1.1	456.992
1.09	481.138
1.08	508.573
1.07	540.626
1.06	579.632
1.05	630.292
1.04	704.486
1.03	851.026

READY

Program notes

(1) This problem can be solved by the direct step method which involves marching up the channel in small steps away from the weir, calculating flow parameters at the boundary of each step from the assumption that, over this short channel reach, flow may be assumed uniform. In this way the friction slope in Equation (4.9) can be evaluated from Manning's formula (Equation (4.4)) as

$$S_f = (Vn/R^{2/3})^2 \qquad (4.18)$$

(2) At line 3 data for the problem are input in the sequence: depth behind weir, depth 1% greater than normal depth (where calculation ends), channel base width, discharge, Manning n-value, channel slope and cotangent of the slope of the channel sides to the vertical. The size of the steps in depth between parameter evaluation is input at line 50 in response to the prompt at line 40.

(3) A running variable I is set equal to unity and the calculation is initiated by setting the distance from the weir as zero. After printing output headings at lines 100 and 110 the initial depth Y1 and starting distance of the calculation, X(1) = 0, are output before commencement of the loop between lines 130 and 250.

(4) In this loop for each new value of depth at the start of a small upstream step the channel cross-section A is evaluated at 140, the wetted perimeter P at 150 and the hydraulic radius R at 160. Calculation of flow velocity V enables the specific energy of the flow E to be found at line 180. Friction slope F is calculated at 190. In the first set of calculations described above, the flow conditions at the weir have been found where the variable I = 1. At line 200, since I = 1 the program is returned to line 130 for the next depth value and subsequent calculation of A, P and R, etc. Now, since I is no longer unity the program proceeds to calculate the distance between the two boundary depths D utilising the E and F values evaluated in the present and previous loops. The position of the end of this step is found at line 220 and the value of Y and X printed at 230. This sequence continues till all steps have been made.

(5) Depending on the size of the step length (which should be of negative sign) a more or less accurate estimate of the length of channel over which these depth changes occur will be obtained as shown by the output for steps in depth of 0.05 m, 0.02 m and 0.01 m.

Example 4.3 SPECENERG: specific energy vs depth curve and y_c

In a laboratory experiment to investigate the occurrence and formation of hydraulic jumps in a rectangular channel it was found necessary to construct the graph of specific energy against depth of flow for a given discharge in order that the energy changes associated with the flow could be illustrated. It was also desirable to establish the value of the critical depth of flow for a given flow rate (i.e. the depth on the specific energy — depth curve corresponding to minimum specific energy). The program below evaluates appropriate depths and corresponding specific energies and also allows an accurate assessment of critical depth to be made.

Example 4.3 SPECENERG: specific energy vs depth curve and y_c 89

```
LIST


SPECENERG  3-JUL-81  15:35:39

10 PRINT "SPECIFIC ENERGY-DEPTH RELATIONSHIPS"
20 PRINT
30 PRINT "CHANNEL BREADTH (MM)=     ";
40 INPUT B
50 PRINT "DISCHARGE (CUMECS)  =    ";
60 INPUT Q
70 PRINT "EVALUATION TO START AT DEPTH YO (MM)=    ";
80 INPUT YO
90 PRINT "EVALUATION TO END AT DEPTH Y1 (MM) = ";
100 INPUT Y1
110 PRINT "LENGTH OF STEP IN DEPTH (MM)=    ";
120 INPUT S
130 PRINT
140 PRINT "DEPTH (MM)",,"SPECIFIC ENERGY (MM)"
150 PRINT "_____"
160 FOR I=YO TO Y1 STEP S
170 E=I+(Q*10^9)^2/(B^2*I^2*2*9810)
180 PRINT I,,E
190 NEXT I
200 PRINT "DO YOU WISH MORE DETAIL OF CRITICAL FLOW? (Y/N) ";
210 INPUT A$
220 IF A$="Y" THEN 70
230 PRINT "ANOTHER RUN WITH NEW Q OR B ? (Y/N) ";
240 INPUT A$
250 IF A$="Y" THEN 30
260 END

READY


RUN


SPECENERG  3-JUL-81  15:36:39

SPECIFIC ENERGY-DEPTH RELATIONSHIPS

CHANNEL BREADTH (MM)=     ? 76
DISCHARGE (CUMECS)  =    ? 0.005
EVALUATION TO START AT DEPTH YO (MM)=    ? 10
EVALUATION TO END AT DEPTH Y1 (MM) = ? 200
LENGTH OF STEP IN DEPTH (MM)=    ? 10

DEPTH (MM)                    SPECIFIC ENERGY (MM)
_____
10                            2216.04
20                            571.511
30                            275.116
40                            177.878
50                            138.242
60                            121.279
70                            115.021
80                            114.469
90                            117.235
100                           122.06
110                           128.232
120                           135.32
130                           143.054
140                           151.255
150                           159.805
160                           168.617
170                           177.633
180                           186.809
190                           196.111
200                           205.515
```

```
DO YOU WISH MORE DETAIL OF CRITICAL FLOW? (Y/N) ? Y
EVALUATION TO START AT DEPTH YO (MM)=    ? 70
EVALUATION TO END AT DEPTH Y1 (MM) = ? 85
LENGTH OF STEP IN DEPTH (MM)=    ? 1

DEPTH (MM)                      SPECIFIC ENERGY (MM)
-------------------------------------------------------
   70                           115.021
   71                           114.762
   72                           114.555
   73                           114.397
   74                           114.286
   75                           114.219
   76                           114.193
   77                           114.208
   78                           114.26
   79                           114.348
   80                           114.469
   81                           114.624
   82                           114.808
   83                           115.023
   84                           115.265
   85                           115.533
DO YOU WISH MORE DETAIL OF CRITICAL FLOW? (Y/N) ? N
ANOTHER RUN WITH NEW Q OR B ? (Y/N) ? N

READY
```

Program notes

(1) The heart of the program is the evaluation of the specific energy level at a particular depth of flow for a given value of discharge given by Equation (4.7) which can be written (for a rectangular channel) as

$$E = y + Q^2/2gb^2y \qquad (4.19)$$

where b is the breadth of the channel.

(2) In response to the prompts at lines 30 and 50 the constants for the problem (breadth and discharge) are input.

(3) It is now necessary to define the limits of the calculation by responding to the prompts at lines 70, 90 and 110. The depth at which calculation should start is determined by the depth of flow upstream of the jump (and should be a value a little less than this). The final depth will also depend on the geometry of the flow. If, for example, the jump is being formed downstream of a sluice gate then a suitable final depth Y1 would be the depth of flow behind the sluice. (Here velocity is small and specific energy E is almost exactly equal to the flow depth.) The step length S should be initially chosen to be fairly long so that the general shape of the curve can be established.

(4) In the loop between lines 160 and 190 the running variable I (= flow depth) is substituted into Equation (4.7) and specific energy is evaluated and printed.

(5) It may be that greater detail of the energy variation in the region of critical flow is required and with a positive response to the prompt at

Example 4.4 NORMDEPTH: evaluation of normal depth in stepped channel   91

line 200 the program returns to line 70 where the calculation can be repeated in the vicinity of the minimum of the curve. (See Figure 4.4(a).)

(6) It is also possible to rerun the program by making a positive response to the prompt at line 230.

(7) The output between the depth limits of 15 and 200 mm with a step length of 5 mm indicates that the critical flow depth lies between 70 and 85 mm. The second set of output is derived from the calculation repeated between these depths with a step length of 1 mm, enabling a more accurate assessment of critical depth and minimum energy to be made.

Example 4.4 NORMDEPTH: evaluation of normal depth in stepped channel

A rectangular channel of breadth 4 m and longitudinal slope 0.0009 has a Manning n-value of 0.015. The channel depth is measured at 1.5 m just upstream of a step down in the channel bed of 0.1 m as shown in Figure 4.8. Estimate the channel discharge, find the normal depth of flow which is established almost immediately downstream of the step and calculate the specific energy of the flow at station 2 in the Figure.

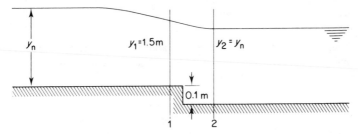

Figure 4.8 Longitudinal channel section for Example 4.4

```
LIST

NORMDEPTH  3-JUL-81  15:46:47

10 PRINT " NORMAL DEPTH EVALUATION"
20 PRINT
30 DATA 4,0.015,.0009,.1,1.5
40 READ B,N,S,Z,Y1
50 PRINT "MAKE INITIAL GUESS AT Y2 (SAY THE SAME AS Y1)  ";
60 INPUT Y2
70 R=(B*Y1)/(B+2*Y1)
80 REM INITIAL ESTIMATE OF DISCHARGE (Q)
90 PRINT "Q","Y2","SPEC EN AT 2"
100 Q=(B*Y1)*R^(2/3)*SQR(S)/N
110 REM SPECIFIC ENERGY AT 1, E1
120 E1=Y1+(Q/(B*Y1))^2/(2*9.81)
130 E2=E1+Z
```

```
140 E=Y2+(Q/(B*Y2))^2/(2*9.81)
150 D=E-E2
160 REM CHECK FOR CONVERGENCE
170 IF ABS(D)>=1.00000E-04 THEN 190
180 GO TO 210
190 Y2=Y2+5.00000E-05
200 GO TO 140
210 PRINT Q,Y2,E
220 R=(B*Y2)/(B+2*Y2)
230 PRINT "DO YOU WISH A FURTHER YS ESTIMATE? (Y/N)";
250 INPUT A$
255 IF A$="Y" THEN 100
260 END

READY


RUN

NORMDEPTH  3-JUL-81  15:47:38

  NORMAL DEPTH EVALUATION

MAKE INITIAL GUESS AT Y2 (SAY THE SAME AS Y1)  ? 1.5
Q             Y2              SPEC EN AT 2
  10.828         1.62437          1.76592
DO YOU WISH A FURTHER YS ESTIMATE? (Y/N)? Y
  11.1559        1.62622          1.77613
DO YOU WISH A FURTHER YS ESTIMATE? (Y/N)? Y
  11.1605        1.62622          1.77626
DO YOU WISH A FURTHER YS ESTIMATE? (Y/N)? Y
  11.1605        1.62622          1.77626
DO YOU WISH A FURTHER YS ESTIMATE? (Y/N)? N

READY
```

Program notes

(1) Input as data at line 30 are the parameters that define the problem − channel breadth, Manning n-value, channel slope, height of step and the depth just upstream of the step.

(2) In the absence of any other information a guess at the channel normal depth of flow (which will be the same a long way upstream of the step as it is downstream of the step) is input as the response to the prompt at line 50 (Y2).

(3) The hydraulic radius of the channel at station 1 is evaluated as R at line 70 and, as the remark REM at line 80 notes, an initial estimate of discharge based on this hydraulic radius is made using the Manning formula at line 100. Using this Q-value the specific energy of the flow at station 1 is found as E1 from which the specific energy at station 2 can be derived at line 130. At line 140 a second estimate of the specific energy is made using the estimated normal depth value Y2 as E. The two values are compared in lines 150−170. If the difference between the two values is greater than 0.0001 m then the program moves to line 190 where the estimate of Y2 is adjusted and the program returned to line 140. If the absolute value of the difference between the two specific energy values is less than 0.0001 m then convergence has been achieved and, at line 210, Q, Y2 and E are printed.

Example 4.5 PROPDEPTH: proportional depth diagram: circular conduit   93

(4) In order to check that the best solution has been found, an amended value of R is evaluated at line 220 and the calculation can be restarted using this new (better) initial estimate by making a positive response to the prompt at line 230.

(5) The first output results indicate a discharge of 10.828 m^3/s. A positive response to the following prompt gives a new, more reliable Q-value of 11.1559 m^3/s. Since this value is obtained using a much more realistic Y2 value succeeding iterations converge very rapidly (here after only one further loop) and the normal depth of flow can be taken as 1.62622 m.

Example 4.5 PROPDEPTH: proportional depth diagram: circular conduit

In a circular conduit such as a sewer which, for the most part does not run full, it is convenient to be able to obtain a value of discharge from a measurement of flow depth, no matter what the diameter of the channel. Thus, for a given roughness characteristic (here the Manning n-value) and slope, it is possible to construct a master plot (from which conduit discharge may be evaluated) known as a proportional depth diagram in which depth and discharges are non-dimensionalised with respect to the pipe diameter and the discharge when running full.

```
LIST

PROPDEPTH   3-JUL-81   15:42:11

10 PRINT "EVALUATION OF PROPORTIONAL DEPTH DIAGRAM: CIRCULAR CONDUIT"
20 PRINT
30 PRINT "DIAMETER OF CONDUIT (M)=";
40 INPUT D
50 PRINT "MANNING N-VALUE = ";
60 INPUT N
70 PRINT "CHANNEL SLOPE= ";
80 INPUT S
90 PRINT
100 Q0=PI*D^(8/3)*SQR(S)/(N*4^(5/3))
110 PRINT "DISCHARGE WHEN FLOWING FULL (M^3/S)= ";
120 PRINT Q0
130 PRINT "Y/D","Q/Q0"
140 PRINT "---------------------------------"
150 X=D/20
160 FOR Y=X TO D STEP X
170 C1=1-2*Y/D
180 T=-ATN(C1/SQR(-C1*C1+1))+1.5708
190 A=D*D*(T-.5*SIN(2*T))/4
200 R=D*(1-.5*SIN(2*T)/(2*T))/4
210 Q=A*R^(2/3)*SQR(S)/N
220 B=Y/D
230 C=Q/Q0
240 PRINT B,C
250 NEXT Y
260 PRINT "DO YOU WISH TO CONTINUE FOR FURTHER PIPES? (Y/N)";
270 INPUT A$
280 IF A$="Y" GO TO 30
290 END
READY
```

```
RUN

PROPDEPTH   3-JUL-81   15:42:46

EVALUATION OF PROPORTIONAL DEPTH DIAGRAM: CIRCULAR CONDUIT

DIAMETER OF CONDUIT (M)=? 1
MANNING N-VALUE = ? 0.015
CHANNEL SLOPE=  ? 0.0009

DISCHARGE WHEN FLOWING FULL (M^3/S)=  .623371
Y/D            Q/QO
----------------------------------------
 .05           .0127774
 .1            .0381278
 .15           .0731461
 .2            .116609
 .25           .167531
 .3            .224965
 .35           .287953
 .4            .355496
 .45           .426548
 .5            .500003
 .55           .574689
 .6            .649356
 .65           .722651
 .7            .793096
 .75           .85903
 .8            .918524
 .85           .969192
 .9            1.00774
 .95           1.02844
DO YOU WISH TO CONTINUE FOR FURTHER PIPES? (Y/N)? Y
DIAMETER OF CONDUIT (M)=? 1.5
MANNING N-VALUE = ? 0.025
CHANNEL SLOPE=  ? 0.0001

DISCHARGE WHEN FLOWING FULL (M^3/S)=  .367581
Y/D            Q/QO
----------------------------------------
 .05           .0127774
 .1            .0381278
 .15           .0731461
 .2            .116609
 .25           .167531
 .3            .224965
 .35           .287953
 .4            .355496
 .45           .426548
 .5            .500002
 .55           .57469
 .6            .649356
 .65           .722651
 .7            .793096
 .75           .85903
 .8            .918524
 .85           .969192
 .9            1.00774
 .95           1.02844
DO YOU WISH TO CONTINUE FOR FURTHER PIPES? (Y/N)? N

READY
```

Program notes

(1) In response to the prompts at lines 30, 50 and 70 the characteristics of the problem are input, from which, by using the Manning equation (Equation (4.4)), it is possible to calculate the discharge when the

Example 4.5 PROPDEPTH: proportional depth diagram: circular conduit   95

conduit is just running full (i.e. hydraulic radius equals D/4) as Q_0 which is printed at line 130.

(2) At line 150 the diameter of the pipe is divided into steps of length S (in this case 20 steps have been selected) and in the loop between lines 160 and 240 the angle subtended by the free water surface T, the area of the flow A and the hydraulic radius of the section R are found. The discharge Q is found from the Manning equation and then at lines 210 and 220 depth and discharge are non-dimensionalised with respect to D and Q_0 before printing at line 230.

(3) The output is plotted in Figure 4.9 for two different n-values. It is interesting to note that for values of Y/D just less than unity, Q/Q_0 is a little greater than one. This is because the addition of a relatively small area of flow at the top of the conduit entails a disproportionately large increase in the wetted perimeter. This causes the hydraulic mean depth, and therefore the velocity, to decrease. The depth discharge curve thus exhibits a maximum just before the conduit runs full.

(4) As demonstrated here, there is a unique curve for circular conduits; other sections exhibit different characteristics.

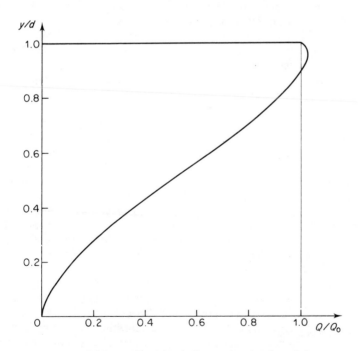

Figure 4.9 Proportional depth diagram for closed conduit

PROBLEMS

(4.1) It is often essential that the normal depth of flow in a channel be known for a given discharge (e.g. when classifying gradually varied flow profiles). For channels in which the breadth is large in relation to the depth of flow, the hydraulic radius of the channel is given (to a good approximation) by the depth of flow and the evaluation of normal depth is relatively straightforward. For many channel geometries, however, the calculation of normal depth can only be achieved by use of an iterative method of solution.

Develop a program that may be used to calculate the normal depth of flow in trapezoidal, rectangular and triangular cross-section channels. (As a test of the validity of the program the data for the channel of Example 4.2 illustrated in Figure 4.7 may be used.)

(4.2) A problem similar to that posed in Problem (4.1) is that of establishing the value of the critical depth of flow in a channel at which discharge is a maximum and specific energy is minimised. At the critical depth the Froude number of the flow $V/\sqrt{gD}$ is unity. (D is the hydraulic depth defined as channel cross-sectional area divided by the free surface top width. V is mean flow velocity.) In all but the simplest cases of channel geometry an analytical solution for critical depth is not possible and a trial and error iterative solution is required.

Write a program to calculate critical flow depths for trapezoidal, rectangular and triangular cross-section channels and also culverts or sewers of circular cross-section.

As examples with which to test the program consider a trapezoidal channel of bottom width 0.5 m with sides sloping at $45°$, a rectangular channel of bottom width 1 m, a triangular channel of vertex angle $30°$ and a circular culvert of 1 m diameter all of which carry a discharge of 2 m^3/s. Critical depths of flow in these examples are 0.750 m, 0.742 m, 1.626 m and 0.815 m respectively.

(4.3) Problems (4.1) and (4.2) yield normal and critical flow depths in channels of different geometry. Calculation of these parameters is important in the classification of flow profiles in gradually varying flow (those illustrated in Figure 4.5). Other factors that may be required for the complete classification of a particular sort of flow are channel bed slope and the actual flow depth at a particular point on the profile. The geometry of the problem may also be required (e.g. is flow under a sluice-gate involved? etc.).

Construct a program that could be used to classify gradually varied flow profiles in accordance with the notation of Figure 4.5. In some of the particular cases it will not be found necessary to know all of the parameters mentioned above before a classification is obtained and the program should be capable of making suitable curtailments in the decision-making procedure where necessary.

(4.4) The previous three problems are concerned with the elements that go towards a complete solution of the channel flow of Example 4.2. Combine the three programs developed for Problems (4.1), (4.2) and (4.3) with that presented in Example 4.2 to make a 'package' suitable for the solution of many similar problems.

(4.5) A wide rectangular channel has a Manning n-value of 0.018 and a slope of 1 in 10000. The channel terminates in a free overfall into a reservoir. At a station a little way upstream of this drop, the depth is critical. If the channel discharge is 2 m^3/s per metre width, how far from the drop will the depth of flow be 10% less than the normal depth of flow?

Solution to this problem could either make use of the program package of Problem (4.4) or the individual unlinked components of that package.

(4.6) In Example 4.5 a program for the generation of a proportional depth diagram for a closed circular conduit is presented. It is also possible to generate a proportional depth diagram for a channel that is not closed over.

Using the Colebrook–White Equation (4.3) write a program to derive the quantities from which a proportional depth diagram could be constructed for a trapezoidal channel of 1 m bottom width and side slope of 1 in 1. It is suggested that the basis of the calculation should be that depths are non-dimensionalised with respect to the base width and the reference discharge is that calculated with a depth of flow of 1 m. The channel has a slope of 0.001 and is of mean roughness height 1 mm. Use the program output to evaluate the flow depth when the channel discharges at 0.3925 m^3/s.

The output generated by the program can be used to analyse any channel of this shape (i.e. trapezoidal, side slope 1 in 1) and bed slope. If a channel of Manning n-value 0.02 is discharging at 10 m^3/s use the program output (in graphical form) to show that the flow depth in this case is approximately 2.25 m if the bottom width of this channel is 1.5 m.

(4.7) Example 4.3 presents a program capable of yielding a table (and hence a graph) of the variation of specific energy with depth in an open channel. It is also possible to use the program to make a good estimate of critical depth of flow which is the depth corresponding to minimum specific energy.

The critical depth of flow corresponds also to the maximum discharge of a channel. Using the data of Example 4.3 modify that program in such a way that a particular value of specific energy may be chosen and a table of the variation of discharge with depth may be drawn up. A means whereby an estimate of critical depth at that energy may be found should also be incorporated.

(4.8) Equation (4.10) represents the relationship between y_1, the depth upstream, y_2, the depth downstream and Fr_1 the Froude number of the flow of a hydraulic jump in a rectangular channel.

Hydraulic jumps can occur in channels of different cross-section. The relationship between the depth ratio y_2/y_1 (written below as r) and the Froude number in a trapezoidal channel is given by

$$Fr_1^2 = \frac{3tr(r+1)(t+r) + 2r(t+r)(r^2+r+1)}{6(t+1)(t+r+1)} \tag{4.20}$$

in which $t = b/zy$, where b is the channel base width and z is the cotangent of the channel side slope.

Using this equation develop a program that can be used to generate values of y_2/y_1 and Fr_1 for channels of trapezoidal, triangular and rectangular cross-section.

(4.9) Write a program that can be used to calculate the hydraulic radius R of a wide variety of different geometry channels to include, for example, rectangular, trapezoidal, triangular, circular and parabolic sections.

It is suggested that the program should use the appropriate geometrical parameters to generate a series of R-values over a range of required depths of flow.

(4.10) Uniform flow in an open channel can be described either by the formula due to Chézy.

$$V = C\sqrt{(RS)} \tag{4.21}$$

where V is mean flow velocity, R is hydraulic radius, S is channel slope and C is a constant for the channel known as Chézy's coefficient or by the equation developed from the Chézy formula known as the Manning formula, Equation (4.4).

An experiment was conducted in a long laboratory channel an end of which could be raised and lowered to alter the bed-slope. The flow-rate down the channel could also be adjusted by means of a valve in the recirculating water supply to the channel. The channel, glass-sided and with a painted metal base, was of width 103 mm. The following measurements were made in the region of uniform flow (in the middle portion of the channel away from entrance and exit effects) of flow depth, discharge rate and bed-slope.

$Q(l/s)$	$S(deg)$	$y(mm)$
1.0	0.5	15.0
	1.0	12.3
	1.5	11.6
	2.0	10.6
	2.5	9.0
	3.0	8.8

1.7	0.5	21.0
	1.0	17.8
	1.5	16.0
	2.0	14.3
	2.5	13.0
	3.0	12.5

Write a program to analyse these data to obtain the most accurate assessment of Chézy coefficient and Manning n-value for this channel.

(**4.11**) An experiment was conducted in the laboratory to calibrate a broad-crested weir of height 100 mm and to compare it with the British Standard BS 3680 which gives the discharge coefficient as

$$C_d = (1 - 2xL/b)(1 - xL/h)^{3/2} \qquad (4.22)$$

where L is length of the crest of the weir, here 275 mm, b is the breadth of the channel (103 mm), x is a factor with the value 0.003 for laboratory channels and h is the height of water above the crest of the structure.

Measurements of channel discharge, Q, were made using a propeller-type flow meter in the water supply circuit and the total depth of water upstream of the weir was measured as y. These results are given below.

$y(mm)$	$Q(l/s)$
125	0.80
141	1.60
153	2.40
163	3.20
174	4.00
184	4.80
193	5.60
201	6.40
209	7.20
216	8.00

When these results were analysed using Equation (4.13) to calculate the theoretical discharge, it was found that the value of discharge coefficient in every case was greater than unity. This result suggests an error of measurement in the system, and investigation of the channel indicated that the flow meter had been miscalibrated.

Write a program to confirm the results of the analysis quoted above and then, using Equation (4.22) evaluate the actual discharge and hence investigate whether the flow meter can be recalibrated by factoring the perceived output from the device.

Chapter 5

Hydraulic machinery

ESSENTIAL THEORY

5.1 Introduction

There are many different sorts of fluid machines and some categorisation is desirable in order to distinguish between individual types. The classification given in Figure 5.1 is based on whether energy is added to or subtracted from the working fluid and whether the machine is of the rotodynamic or positive displacement type.

	ENERGY ADDED	ENERGY TRANSFERRED	ENERGY SUBTRACTED
ROTODYNAMIC	Pumps-Fans-Compressors (1)Uncased: propellers screws (2)Cased: axial, mixed radial flow	(5)Hydraulic coupling (6)Torque converter	Turbines (7)Impulse : pelton windmill (8)Reaction: axial (Kaplan) mixed (Francis) radial (Banki)
POSITIVE DISPLACEMENT	Pumps-Compressors (3)Reciprocating: crank direct drive ,etc. (4)Rotary: screw, etc.		Motors (9) Piston,etc.

Figure 5.1 Classification of hydraulic machines [after Douglas, Gasiorek, Swaffield, *Fluid Mechanics,* Pitman, (1979)]

In axial flow machines fluid enters and leaves parallel to the axis of the impeller while in radial (centrifugal) flow machines fluid enters parallel to and leaves normal to the impeller axis. This chapter will be concerned principally with the performance and operation of hydraulic machines of categories 2, 7 and 8, i.e. rotodynamic pumps and turbines with water as the working fluid.

5.2 Elementary theory

Real fluid flow through the impeller of a pump or turbine is three-dimensional. In order to simplify the analysis, such flow is considered

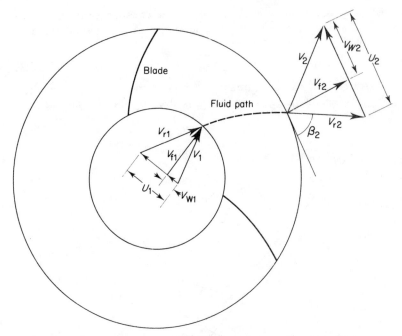

Figure 5.2 Inlet and outlet velocity diagrams for centrifugal impeller

as one-dimensional and is usually represented by means of inlet and outlet fluid velocity triangles such as those shown for the centrifugal impeller in Figure 5.2. Velocities u are the blade tip tangential velocities, velocities v are absolute fluid velocities, velocities v_f and v_w are radial and tangential fluid velocities while v_r are fluid velocities relative to the impeller blades. Suffices 1 and 2 refer to inlet and outlet of the impeller respectively. Analysis of this gives Euler's equation for the theoretical (or Euler) head developed by the pump.

$$E = (u_2 v_{w2} - u_1 v_{w1})/g \tag{5.1}$$

This method of analysis applies to radial and axial flow pumps and turbines. (In the case of turbines, adjustment is required to the signs of the equation components.)

By assuming that the inlet tangential velocity component (v_{w1}) is zero in a centrifugal impeller, it can be shown that the theoretical head developed by the pump, H_{th}, is given by

$$H_{th} = \frac{u_2}{g}\left(u_2 - \frac{Q}{A_2}\cot\beta_2\right) \tag{5.2}$$

where Q is the pump discharge, A_2 is the cross-sectional area of the outlet and β_2 is the blade angle at outlet. At a constant speed of rotation

$$H_{th} = C_1 - C_2 Q \tag{5.3}$$

where C_1 and C_2 are constants for a given speed and the theoretical head versus discharge characteristic is given by the straight line A in Figure 5.3.

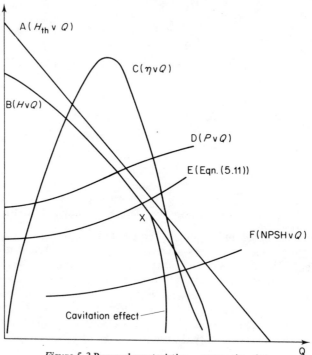

Figure 5.3 Pump characteristics – composite plot

5.3 Performance

Because of the simplifying assumptions made in the analysis and the many sources of head loss that occur in practice, the actual characteristics are more typically given by curve B in Figure 5.3. Losses occur both from hydraulic sources (boundary layer friction and separation, recirculation of fluid in the impeller, etc.) and mechanical sources (bearings and sealing glands, etc.) so that, for a pump, only a fraction of the input power P produces useful fluid power ($\rho g H Q$) giving an efficiency

$$\eta_P = \rho g H Q / P \tag{5.4}$$

In the case of a turbine not all the fluid power input is converted to useful output power and efficiency is written

$$\eta_T = P / \rho g H Q \tag{5.5}$$

The characteristics that define how a pump performs are summarised by curves B, C and D in Figure 5.3 and by curves A, B and C in Figure 5.4 for a turbine. The point of peak efficiency on the figures corresponds to the machine design point.

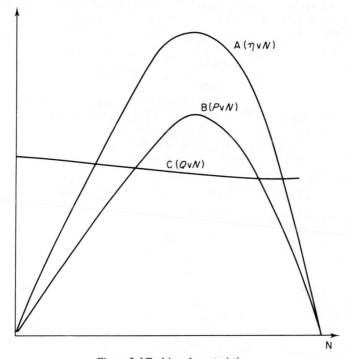

Figure 5.4 Turbine characteristics

5.4 Dimensionless coefficients and similarity

In order to compare the performance of geometrically similar machines, dimensional analysis is used to relate parameters relevant to machine performance. Thus, power transferred between fluid and impeller, P, can be related to the volume flow rate through the machine Q, the head difference across the machine H, (usually included in the analysis as gH equivalent to energy per unit mass of fluid), the rotational speed of the impeller N, impeller diameter D, fluid density, absolute viscosity and bulk elastic modulus ρ, μ and K respectively and the roughness height of the machine passages k, by the general expression

$$P = \phi(Q,\, gH,\, N,\, D,\, \rho,\, \mu,\, K,\, k) \qquad (5.6)$$

Dimensional analysis of this relationship yields

$$\frac{P}{\rho N^3 D^5} = \phi\left[\left(\frac{Q}{ND^3}\right),\, \left(\frac{gH}{N^2 D^2}\right),\, \left(\frac{\mu}{ND^2 \rho}\right),\, \left(\frac{K}{\rho N^2 D^2}\right),\, \left(\frac{k}{D}\right)\right] \qquad (5.7)$$

This equation can be simplified if the working fluid is considered incompressible and of low viscosity and the machine passages are smooth to give

$$\frac{P}{\rho N^3 D^5} = \phi\left[\left(\frac{Q}{ND^3}\right),\, \left(\frac{gH}{N^2 D^2}\right)\right] \qquad (5.8)$$

The relationship between these groups is determined experimentally and constitutes a set of dimensionless performance characteristics representing a whole family of geometrically similar machines.

It is also possible to make comparison between different machine families by means of a type number or specific speed derived from a combination of the non-dimensional characteristics in Equation (5.8), allowing some assessment of a given machine's suitability for a particular task.

For a pump, specific speed is given by

$$n_{SP} = \left(\frac{Q}{ND^3}\right)^{1/2} \div \left(\frac{gH}{N^2 D^2}\right)^{3/4} = \frac{NQ^{1/2}}{(gH)^{3/4}} \qquad (5.9)$$

and is the speed of a model of the pump proportioned to deliver unit volume per second of fluid at unit head.

For a turbine, specific speed is given by

$$n_{ST} = \left(\frac{P}{\rho N^3 D^5}\right)^{1/2} \div \left(\frac{gH}{N^2 D^2}\right)^{5/4} = \frac{NP^{1/2}}{\rho^{1/2}(gH)^{5/4}} \qquad (5.10)$$

and is the speed of a model of the turbine proportioned to deliver unit power under unit head. It should be noted that a specific speed can be evaluated for any point on a characteristic but, since a machine is designed to operate at a certain head and discharge, etc. it is these 'design point' values that are used in calculating specific speeds.

Typical specific speed ranges, based on design point data (using rad/s, metres, cubic metres/s and watts as basic units), are shown in Figure 5.5.

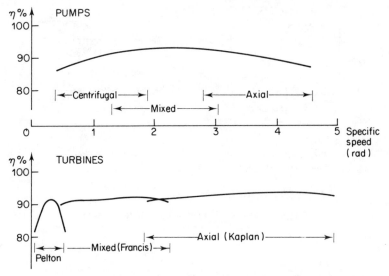

Figure 5.5 Specific speed ranges of pumps and turbines [after Douglas, Gasiorek, Swaffield, *Fluid Mechanics*, Pitman, (1979)]

5.5 Pipe-machine systems

If a pump is required to raise water from a lower to an upper reservoir it must generate sufficient head to overcome first the height difference between the two reservoir levels (the static lift Δz) and second the frictional and other head losses in the associated pipe system which will generally be of the form KQ^2. The value of K will be derived by considering individual sources of loss in the system. The pump must therefore supply a head

$$H = \Delta z + KQ^2 \qquad (5.11)$$

where the right-hand side of the equation is known as the system resistance. In order for the pump to be operating with reasonable efficiency the system characteristic and machine characteristic at a given speed must intersect near the machine design point (see curve E on Figure 5.3). If this is not possible with an existing configuration of machine and piping then machine combination should be considered in order to achieve better overall performance. If pumps are connected in parallel then the system discharge can be increased as shown in Figure 5.6(a). The combined characteristic for two different pumps so connected is given in Figure 5.7. For pumps connected in series the lift capability of the system is enhanced as shown in Figure 5.6(b) and the

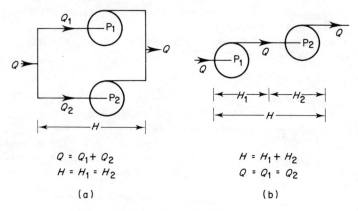

$$Q = Q_1 + Q_2 \qquad\qquad H = H_1 + H_2$$
$$H = H_1 = H_2 \qquad\qquad Q = Q_1 = Q_2$$

(a)   (b)

Figure 5.6(a) Pumps in parallel (*b*) Pumps in series

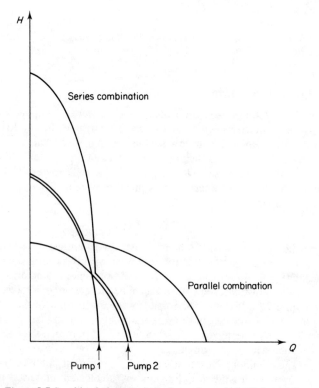

Figure 5.7 Combined characteristics for series and parallel operation

Example 5.1 PUMPEFFIC: calculation of pump efficiency, etc.   107

combined characteristic for two different pumps is given in Figure 5.7. Analysis of the performance of each individual component in conjunction with the system characteristic will indicate how much improvement has been effected by any changes.

5.6 Cavitation in machines

Cavitation is the local vaporisation of a liquid when the absolute value of pressure falls below the vapour pressure of the liquid at a given temperature and is seen as small bubbles in the body of the fluid. When such bubbles move to a region of higher pressure they collapse violently generating high intensity pressure waves. The occurrence of cavitation in a hydraulic machine results in a loss in performance and can cause considerable damage if allowed to persist.

As an example of the conditions that will cause cavitation, consider a rotodynamic pump where the point of lowest pressure is at the inlet. The quantity known as net positive suction head (NPSH) is a measure of the absolute head at the inlet before cavitation occurs where

$$\text{NPSH} = (p_i - p_{\text{vap}})/\rho g \qquad (5.12)$$

in which p_i is inlet pressure and p_{vap} is the pressure at which cavitation will occur. By considering the factors which determine p_i this can be written

$$\text{NPSH} = p_{\text{at}}/\rho g - H_s - p_{\text{vap}}/\rho g \qquad (5.13)$$

where p_{at} is atmospheric pressure and H_s is the suction head required to lift the fluid from its initial level up to the level of the pump inlet and is comprised of a static component (suction lift) and dynamic head loss terms.

Thus, if the total head requirement is H, no more than the NPSH part should be used on the suction side if cavitation is to be avoided. The fall-off in pump performance can be demonstrated by partly closing the pump inlet pipe thus introducing extra resistance. At point X on curve B of Figure 5.3 the characteristic departs from the norm and no further increase in outlet opening will increase the flow. Such deviation can be made to occur earlier by introducing even greater resistance on the suction side of the machine. Also plotted on Figure 5.3 is a graph of NPSH versus discharge (curve F) which shows the minimum NPSH required by the pump to avoid cavitation.

WORKED EXAMPLES

Example 5.1 PUMPEFFIC: calculation of pump efficiency, etc.

In an experiment to determine the operating characteristics of a centrifugal pump, tests were conducted at several speeds and at a series of different discharges at each speed. For each discharge the total head across the pump (the sum of the suction and delivery heads) and the 'brake load' (generated by the motor driving the pump) was measured. The brake load was registered on a spring balance connected via a torque arm to the body of the pump motor. For this pump the total torque arm L was measured at 0.150 m.

Write a program to analyse the data from a test at a given speed to produce the efficiency of the pump at different discharges and hence determine the design point at a particular speed.

Data from one of the tests was as follows

Speed: 3000 *rev/min*

Brake Load (N)	Head (m)	Discharge (1/s)
12.0	29.2	0
14.2	28.9	0.5
16.0	28.2	1.0
18.0	27.9	1.5
20.1	27.2	2.0
22.2	25.8	2.5
24.2	24.1	3.0
26.2	21.8	3.5
28.5	19.6	4.0
30.4	17.0	4.5
32.0	15.0	4.7

```
LIST

PUMPEFFIC  6-JUL-81  08:58:19

10 PRINT "EVALUATION OF PUMP EFFICIENCY"
20 PRINT
30 PRINT "TORQUE ARM LENGTH (M) =   ";
40 INPUT L
50 PRINT "WORKING FLUID DENSITY (KG/M^3)=   ";
60 INPUT R
70 PRINT
80 PRINT "SPEED OF PUMP (RPM)=  ";
90 INPUT N
100 PRINT
110 DIM F(50),H(50),Q(50),O(50),P(50),E(50)
120 PRINT "HOW MANY SETS OF DATA AT THIS SPEED?";
130 INPUT M
140 PRINT
150 PRINT "HEAD","DISCHARGE","POWER OUT","POWER IN","EFFICIENCY"
160 PRINT "(M)","(L/S)","(W)","(W)","(%)"
170 PRINT "----------------------------------------------------------------"
180 FOR J=1 TO M
190 READ F(J),H(J),Q(J)
200 REM EVALUATE POWER INPUT
210 P(J)=2*PI*(N/60)*L*F(J)
220 REM EVALUATE POWER OUTPUT
230 O(J)=R*9.81*H(J)*Q(J)*1.00000E-03
240 REM EVALUATE EFFICIENCY
250 E(J)=O(J)/P(J)*100
260 PRINT H(J),Q(J),O(J),P(J),E(J)
```

Example 5.1 PUMPEFFIC: calculation of pump efficiency, etc.   109

```
270 NEXT J
280 PRINT
290 PRINT "IS THERE ANY FURTHER DATA TO PROCESS?   (Y/N)";
300 INPUT A$
310 IF A$="Y" THEN 70
320 DATA 12,29.2,0,14.2,28.9,0.5,16,28.2,1,18,27.9,1.5
330 DATA 20.1,27.2,2,22.2,25.8,2.5,24.2,24.1,3,26.2,21.8,3.5
340 DATA 28.5,19.6,4,30.4,17,4.5,32,15,4.7
350 DATA
READY


RUN

PUMPEFFIC   6-JUL-81   08:59:05

EVALUATION OF PUMP EFFICIENCY

TORQUE ARM LENGTH (M)  =    ? 0.150
WORKING FLUID DENSITY (KG/M^3)=    ? 1000

SPEED OF PUMP (RPM)=   ? 3000

HOW MANY SETS OF DATA AT THIS SPEED?? 11
```

HEAD (M)	DISCHARGE (L/S)	POWER OUT (W)	POWER IN (W)	EFFICIENCY (%)
29.2	0	0	565.487	0
28.9	.5	141.754	669.159	21.184
28.2	1	276.642	753.982	36.6908
27.9	1.5	410.548	848.23	48.4006
27.2	2	533.664	947.19	56.3418
25.8	2.5	632.745	1046.15	60.4832
24.1	3	709.263	1140.4	62.1943
21.8	3.5	748.503	1234.65	60.6249
19.6	4	769.104	1343.03	57.2663
17	4.5	750.465	1432.57	52.3861
15	4.7	691.605	1507.96	45.8635

```
IS THERE ANY FURTHER DATA TO PROCESS?   (Y/N)? N

READY
```

Program notes

(1) The program is constructed in such a way that it can be used for a series of experiments on the same pump without need to call 'RUN' for each new set of data. Thus, the constants for the system, torque arm and density of the working fluid, are entered at lines 40 and 60 as L and R before the speed N and number of sets of data are input at line 90 and 130 in response to the prompts.

(2) In the loop between lines 170 and 250 data are read in groups of 3 and operated on to evaluate power in and out and efficiency. Mechanical power input is given by the product of torque T multiplied by angular velocity ω.

Thus, here

$$P = (FL) \times 2\pi(N/60) \qquad (5.14)$$

Results are printed at line 240.

(3) When M sets of data have been analysed the prompt at line 270 can be used to initiate further analysis by returning to line 70 and subsequently reading more data from line 350 onwards.

(4) The results of the analysis of this set of data are plotted in Figure 5.8 from which it will be seen that the pump design point is at a head of 24 m and a discharge of 3.0 1/s. Note also that this does not correspond to the maximum fluid power output which continues to rise up to a discharge of approximately 4.0 1/s.

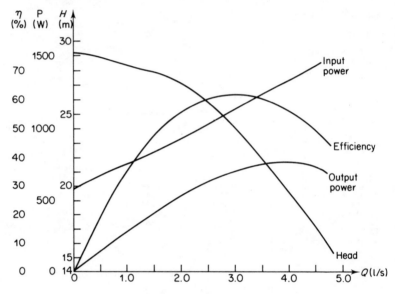

Figure 5.8 Results of analysis of Example 5.1

Example 5.2 NONDIMCHA: non-dimensionalisation of pump characteristics

A pumped storage water supply system requires the design of a set of pumps to handle large volumes of water. The pumps that have been proposed are of 2 m diameter and in order to assess their performance a pair of geometrically similar models are built of diameters 0.140 m and 0.102 m. These models are to be tested over a range of operating speeds, heads and discharges in order to establish a set of non-dimensional operating characteristics for the family. The information so obtained can then be used to predict the behaviour of the large pumps in service.

The experimental configuration is similar to that of Example 5.1 with a torque arm here of 0.165 m. Details of four of the tests are given below.

Pump 1 – diameter 0.140 m

	Speed 1700 rev/min			Speed 2500 rev/min	
Head (m)	Discharge (1/s)	Brake load (N)	Head (m)	Discharge (1/s)	Brake load (N)
4.2	3.4	11.2	12.2	4.4	21.5
6.6	2.7	9.8	16.3	3.5	19.0
8.3	2.0	7.7	18.7	2.6	15.5
9.2	1.4	6.3	20.4	1.7	11.5
9.9	0.7	4.8	21.6	0.8	8.7
10.1	0	2.5	21.7	0	6.6

Pump 2 – diameter 0.102 m

	Speed 1700 rev/min			Speed 3000 rev/min	
Head (m)	Discharge (1/s)	Brake load (N)	Head (m)	Discharge (1/s)	Brake load (N)
0.4	1.6	2.7	4.2	2.5	7.5
2.4	1.3	2.3	9.9	2.0	6.5
3.7	1.0	1.9	12.9	1.5	5.3
4.6	0.7	1.5	15.1	1.0	4.0
5.3	0.3	1.0	16.5	0	1.5
5.3	0	0.6			

Write a program to evaluate the power, head and discharge non-dimensional parameters for these tests and hence plot the dimensionless characteristics for the family of machines in order to estimate the discharge capability and efficiency of one of the large pumps running at 400 rev/min under a head of 50 m.

```
LIST

NONDIMCHA  6-JUL-81  09:05:09

10 PRINT "EVALUATION OF NON-DIMENSIONAL PUMP CHARACTERISTICS"
20 PRINT
30 PRINT "TORQUE ARM (M) =    ";
40 INPUT L
50 PRINT
60 PRINT "IMPELLER DIAMETER (M)=   ";
70 INPUT D
80 PRINT "PUMP SPEED (RPM)  =   ";
90 INPUT N
100 PRINT
110 DIM H(100),Q(100),F(100),A(100),B(100),C(100)
120 PRINT "HOW MANY SETS OF DATA IN THIS BLOC?  ";
130 INPUT M
140 PRINT
150 PRINT "GH/(ND^2)","Q/(ND^3)","P/(RN^3D^5)"
160 PRINT "_____"
170 FOR I=1 TO M
180 READ H(I),Q(I),F(I)
190 A(I)=(9.81*H(I))/(((N/60)*D)^2)
200 B(I)=Q(I)*1.00000E-03/(((N/60)*(D^3)))
```

```
210 C(I)=F(I)*L*2*PI*(N/60)/((N/60)^3*(D^5)*1000)
220 PRINT A(I),B(I),C(I)
230 NEXT I
240 PRINT "_____"
250 PRINT
260 PRINT "ANY FURTHER DATA TO ANALYSE?    (Y/N)";
270 INPUT A$
280 IF A$="Y" THEN 50
290 DATA 4.2,3.4,11.2,6.6,2.7,9.8,8.3,2,7.7,9.2,1.4,6.3,9.9,.7,4.8,10.1,0,2.5
300 DATA 12.2,4.4,21.5,16.3,3.5,19,18.7,2.6,15.5,20.4,1.7,11.5,21.6,.8,8.7
310 DATA 21.7,0,6.6,0.4,1.6,2.7,2.4,1.3,2.3,3.7,1.0,1.9,4.6,0.7,1.5,5.3,0.3,1
320 DATA 5.3,0,0.6,4.2,2.5,7.5,9.9,2,6.5,12.9,1.5,5.3,15.1,1,4,16.5,0,1.5
330 END

READY


RUN

NONDIMCHA   6-JUL-81   09:06:00

EVALUATION OF NON-DIMENSIONAL PUMP CHARACTERISTICS

TORQUE ARM (M) =    ? 0.165

IMPELLER DIAMETER (M)=    ? 0.140
PUMP SPEED (RPM)  =    ? 1700

HOW MANY SETS OF DATA IN THIS BLOC?  ? 6

GH/(ND^2)      Q/(ND^3)       P/(RN^3D^5)
------------------------------------------------
  2.61859      .0437318       .268934
  4.11492      .0347282       .235318
  5.17483      .0257246       .184892
  5.73595      .0180072       .151276
  6.17238      9.00360E-03    .115258
  6.29708      0              .06003
------------------------------------------------

ANY FURTHER DATA TO ANALYSE?   (Y/N)? Y

IMPELLER DIAMETER (M)=    ? 0.140
PUMP SPEED (RPM)  =    ? 2500

HOW MANY SETS OF DATA IN THIS BLOC?  ? 6

GH/(ND^2)      Q/(ND^3)       P/(RN^3D^5)
------------------------------------------------
  3.51719      .038484        .238718
  4.69919      .0306123       .21096
  5.3911       .0227405       .172099
  5.8812       .0148688       .127686
  6.22715      6.99709E-03    .0965974
  6.25598      0              .0732808
------------------------------------------------

ANY FURTHER DATA TO ANALYSE?   (Y/N)? Y

IMPELLER DIAMETER (M)=    ? 0.102
PUMP SPEED (RPM)  =    ? 1700

HOW MANY SETS OF DATA IN THIS BLOC?  ? 6

GH/(ND^2)      Q/(ND^3)       P/(RN^3D^5)
------------------------------------------------
   .469822     .0532135       .315814
  2.81893      .043236        .269027
  4.34585      .0332584       .222239
  5.40295      .0232809       .175452
  6.22514      9.97753E-03    .116968
  6.22514      0              .0701809
------------------------------------------------

ANY FURTHER DATA TO ANALYSE?   (Y/N)? Y
```

```
IMPELLER DIAMETER (M)=   ? 0.102
PUMP SPEED (RPM)   =    ? 3000

HOW MANY SETS OF DATA IN THIS BLOC?  ? 5

GH/(ND^2)      Q/(ND^3)        P/(RN^3D^5)
------------------------------------------------------
  1.58408       .0471161        .281698
  3.73391       .0376929        .244139
  4.8654        .0282697        .199067
  5.69516       .0188464        .150239
  6.22318       0               .0563397
------------------------------------------------------

ANY FURTHER DATA TO ANALYSE?    (Y/N)? N

READY
```

Program notes

(1) This program is of the same basic format as that of Example 5.1, in that information particular to an experiment is input in response to the prompts at lines 60, 80 and 120 (i.e. diameter D, pump speed N and number of sets of data M) while experimental readings of head H, discharge Q and brake load F are input as data and read as part of the loop between lines 170 and 230. Non-dimensional parameters are printed at line 220.

(2) Depending on the response to the prompt at line 260 the program returns to line 50 for the analysis of a further bloc of data if necessary.

(3) The tabulated output is plotted in Figure 5.9 where it will be seen

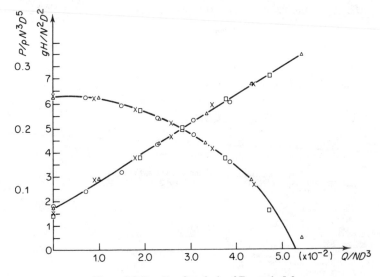

Figure 5.9 Results of analysis of Example 5.2

that there is only a very little scatter, and scaling using these parameters is valid. The graph of results may be used to assess the performance of the prototype pump by the following simple calculation when $H = 50$ m and $N = 400$ rev/min for a 2 m diameter pump $gH/N^2D^2 = 2.76$ (N is here expressed in rev/s). Thus, from the graph $Q/ND^3 = 4.325 \times 10^{-2}$ giving $Q = 2.31$ m^3/s.

Thus, the fluid power output at this point is ρgHQ which is found to be 1131.4 kW. From the non-dimensional power characteristic $P/\rho N^3 D^5$ is read as 0.264 giving a mechanical power input $P = 2503$ kW. The large pump thus operates with an efficiency of 46%.

Example 5.3 PUMPOPPT: evaluation of pump operating point

The characteristics of a centrifugal pump can be represented by a quadrant of an ellipse of equation

$$(H/8)^2 + (Q/0.025)^2 = 1 \qquad (5.15)$$

where H is head in metres and Q is discharge in cumecs.

The pump is required to lift water from a river up to a reservoir whose free surface is 4 m above that of the river. Pipes of diameter 0.2 m and absolute roughness 0.008 mm are available and a length of 1200 m is required to transport the water from river to reservoir. Calculate what the discharge from the pipe into the reservoir will be under these conditions.

The dynamic viscosity of water may be taken as 1.14×10^{-3} kg/ms.

LIST

```
PUMPOPPT    6-JUL-81    09:14:42

10 PRINT "EVALUATION OF PUMP OPERATING POINT"
20 PRINT
30 DATA 8.0E-6,0.2,1200,4
40 READ K,D,L,Z
50 PRINT "RELATIVE ROUGHNESS (K/D)  =  ";
60 R=K/D
70 PRINT R
80 PRINT
90 PRINT "INPUT ESTIMATE OF FRICTION FACTOR FROM MOODY DIAGRAM (FIG 3.3)"
100 INPUT F
110 REM HEAD LOSS DUE TO FRICTION IS F*L*Q^2/(3*D^5)
120 REM SYSTEM CHARACTERISTIC H1=Z+F*L*Q^2/(3*D^5)
130 REM PUMP CHARACTERISTIC IS (H/8)^2+(Q/0.025)^2=1
140 PRINT "CHOOSE START, FINISH AND STEP LENGTH FOR HEAD CALCULATION"
150 INPUT A,B,C
160 PRINT
170 PRINT "Q (M^3/S)","H1 (M)","H(M)"
180 PRINT "-----------------------------------------------"
190 FOR Q=A TO B STEP C
200 H1=Z+F*L*Q^2/(3*D^5)
210 H=8*SQR(1-(Q/.025)^2)
220 PRINT Q,H1,H
230 NEXT Q
```

Example 5.3 PUMPOPPT: evaluation of pump operating point 115

```
240 PRINT
250 PRINT "EXAMINE TABLE, SELECT BEST Q-VALUE AND THUS FIND REYNOLDS NO"
260 PRINT "BEST Q-VALUE  =  ";
270 INPUT Q1
280 V=4*Q1/(PI*D^2)
290 R1=1000*V*D/1.14000E-03
300 PRINT "CORRESPONDING REYNOLDS NUMBER=    ";
310 PRINT R1
320 PRINT "IS THERE FURTHER ITERATION REQUIRED? (IE COMPARE RE & F) (Y/N)";
330 INPUT A$
340 IF A$="N" THEN 410
350 PRINT "REVISED VALUE OF FRICTION FACTOR=    ";
360 INPUT F
370 PRINT "DO YOU WISH TO ALTER LIMITS/STEP IN LINE 190?   (Y/N)";
380 INPUT B$
390 IF B$="Y" THEN 140
400 IF B$="N" THEN 170
410 END

READY


RUN


PUMPOPPT   6-JUL-81  09:15:38

EVALUATION OF PUMP OPERATING POINT

RELATIVE ROUGHNESS (K/D)  =   4.00000E-05

INPUT ESTIMATE OF FRICTION FACTOR FROM MOODY DIAGRAM (FIG 3.3)
? 0.0025
CHOOSE START, FINISH AND STEP LENGTH FOR HEAD CALCULATION
? 0.015,0.025,0.001

Q (M^3/S)      H1 (M)        H(M)
-------------------------------------------
 .015         4.70313       6.4
 .016         4.8           6.147
 .017         4.90313       5.8657
 .018         5.0125        5.55179
 .019         5.12813       5.19938
 .02          5.25          4.8
 .021         5.37813       4.34069
 .022         5.5125        3.79979
 .023         5.65313       3.13535
 .024         5.8           2.24

EXAMINE TABLE, SELECT BEST Q-VALUE AND THUS FIND REYNOLDS NO
BEST Q-VALUE  =  ? 0.019
CORRESPONDING REYNOLDS NUMBER=     106103
IS THERE FURTHER ITERATION REQUIRED? (IE COMPARE RE & F) (Y/N)? Y
REVISED VALUE OF FRICTION FACTOR=   ? 0.004
DO YOU WISH TO ALTER LIMITS/STEP IN LINE 190?   (Y/N)? Y
CHOOSE START, FINISH AND STEP LENGTH FOR HEAD CALCULATION
? 0.015,0.020,0.0005

Q (M^3/S)      H1 (M)        H(M)
-------------------------------------------
 .015         5.125         6.4
 .0155        5.20125       6.27681
 .016         5.28          6.147
 .0165        5.36125       6.01013
 .017         5.445         5.8657
 .0175        5.53125       5.71314
 .018         5.62          5.55179
 .0185        5.71125       5.38086
 .019         5.805         5.19939
 .0195        5.90125       5.00624
 .02          6             4.8
```

```
EXAMINE TABLE, SELECT BEST Q-VALUE AND THUS FIND REYNOLDS NO
BEST Q-VALUE  =  ? 0.018
CORRESPONDING REYNOLDS NUMBER=       100519
IS THERE FURTHER ITERATION REQUIRED? (IE COMPARE RE & F) (Y/N)? Y
REVISED VALUE OF FRICTION FACTOR=    ? 0.0041
DO YOU WISH TO ALTER LIMITS/STEP IN LINE 190?   (Y/N)? Y
CHOOSE START, FINISH AND STEP LENGTH FOR HEAD CALCULATION
? 0.0175,0.0182,0.00005

Q (M^3/S)      H1 (M)          H(M)
-----------------------------------------
  .0175        5.56953         5.71314
  .01755       5.57851         5.69742
  .0176        5.58752         5.6816
  .01765       5.59655         5.66569
  .0177        5.60561         5.6497
  .01775       5.6147          5.63361
  .0178        5.62381         5.61743
  .01785       5.63294         5.60116
  .0179        5.6421          5.5848
  .01795       5.65129         5.56834
  .018         5.6605          5.55179
  .01805       5.66974         5.53514
  .0181        5.679           5.5184
  .01815       5.68829         5.50155

EXAMINE TABLE, SELECT BEST Q-VALUE AND THUS FIND REYNOLDS NO
BEST Q-VALUE  =  ? 0.0178
CORRESPONDING REYNOLDS NUMBER=        99402
IS THERE FURTHER ITERATION REQUIRED? (IE COMPARE RE & F) (Y/N)? N

READY
```

Program notes

(1) The main problem here is to match the pump and system characteristic while being initially uncertain of the pipe friction factor which
can only be roughly estimated at the start of the calculation procedure.
Successive iterations to find the real operating point use a better
estimate of friction factor each time.

(2) Data concerning the pipe system are read at line 40 from the data
at line 30. K is roughness height (in metres), D is pipe diameter, L is the
length of the pipe run and Z is the static lift between river and
reservoir.

(3) With no information about the Reynolds number of the flow an
estimate of friction factor F is required from the Moody diagram (Figure
3.3) using the relative roughness value (K/D) to give some idea of the
size of the term which is input at line 100.

(4) The remarks in lines 110–130 set out the head-discharge relationships for the pump and pipes. The terms H1 (the system head) and H
(the pump head) corresponding to a discharge Q are to be evaluated for
a given Q and in order to obtain an initial estimate of the operating
point, limits A, B to the value of Q with fairly large steps (C) between
them are input at line 150.

(5) The loop between lines 190 and 230 evaluates the system and
pump head at each Q-value and prints them as a table. In response to

the prompt at line 250 the table is examined and the Q-value which gives values of H1 and H that are closest to each other is read and input as Q1 at line 270.

(6) Using this value the Reynolds number corresponding to this discharge is evaluated and printed at line 310 and is used in conjunction with the K/D value to obtain a better estimate of friction factor if required.

(7) The limits of the loop may be altered at this stage (line 370) to obtain a more accurate estimate of Q and the process can continue until acceptable convergence is obtained. In this case the best value of the system discharge is 0.0178 m³/s. Any further iteration could proceed without the need to alter the friction factor, only adjustment to the Q-value limits and step length being necessary.

Example 5.4 PUMPPRED: prediction of geometrically similar pump characteristics

A centrifugal pump has an impeller diameter of 0.4 m and, when running at a speed of 2000 rev/min, its characteristics are as follows

$Q\ (m^3/s)$	$H\ (m)$
0	12.0
0.1	11.8
0.2	11.6
0.3	11.2
0.4	10.7
0.5	10.0
0.6	9.2
0.7	8.4
0.8	7.0
0.9	4.4
1.0	3.0
1.1	0

Write a program to obtain the characteristics of a geometrically similar pump of diameter 0.5 m running at 2500 rev/min.

```
LIST

PUMPPRED    6-JUL-81   09:36:43

10 PRINT "PREDICTION OF 'SAME-GEOMETRY' PUMP CHARACTERISTICS"
20 PRINT
30 PRINT "DIAMETER OF ORIGINAL PUMP (M)=";
40 INPUT D1
50 PRINT "SPEED OF ORIGINAL PUMP (RPM) =";
60 INPUT N1
70 PRINT
```

```
80 PRINT "DIAMETER OF NEW PUMP (M)=";
90 INPUT D2
100 PRINT "SPEED OF NEW PUMP (RPM)=";
110 INPUT N2
120 C1=(N2/N1)*(D2/D1)^3
130 C2=((N2/N1)*(D2/D1))^2
140 DIM Q(25),H(25)
150 PRINT
160 PRINT "NUMBER OF SETS OF DATA AVAILABLE = ";
170 INPUT N
180 PRINT
190 PRINT "NEW CHARACTERISTICS ","Q(M^3/S)","H(M)"
200 PRINT "----------------------------------------------------------------"
210 FOR I=1 TO N
220 READ Q(I),H(I)
230 Q(I)=C1*Q(I)
240 H(I)=C2*H(I)
250 PRINT ,,Q(I),H(I)
260 NEXT I
270 PRINT "----------------------------------------------------------------"
280 DATA 0,12,.1,11.8,.2,11.6,.3,11.2,.4,10.7,.5,10
290 DATA .6,9.2,.7,8.4,.8,7,.9,4.4,1,3,1.1,0
300 END
```

READY

RUN

PUMPPRED   6-JUL-81   09:37:23

PREDICTION OF 'SAME-GEOMETRY' PUMP CHARACTERISTICS

DIAMETER OF ORIGINAL PUMP (M)=? 0.4
SPEED OF ORIGINAL PUMP (RPM) =? 2000

DIAMETER OF NEW PUMP (M)=? 0.5
SPEED OF NEW PUMP (RPM)=? 2500

NUMBER OF SETS OF DATA AVAILABLE = ? 12

NEW CHARACTERISTICS	Q(M^3/S)	H(M)
	0	29.2969
	.244141	28.8086
	.488281	28.3203
	.732422	27.3438
	.976563	26.1231
	1.2207	24.4141
	1.46484	22.4609
	1.70898	20.5078
	1.95313	17.0898
	2.19727	10.7422
	2.44141	7.32422
	2.68555	0

READY

Program notes

(1) In response to the prompts between lines 30 and 100 the diameter and running speeds of the two pumps are input.

(2) Prediction of the performance of the second pump is based on the equality of the non-dimensional head and discharge coefficients. Thus,

where suffix 1 refers to the original pump and suffix 2 to the new pump, it is necessary that

$$Q_1/N_1 D_1^3 = Q_2/N_2 D_2^3 \tag{5.16}$$

i.e.

$$Q_2 = (N_2/N_1)(D_2/D_1)^3 Q_1 \tag{5.17}$$

and

$$gH_1/N_1^2 D_1^2 = gH_2/N_2^2 D_2^2 \tag{5.18}$$

i.e.

$$H_2 = (N_2/N_1)^2 (D_2/D_1)^2 H_1 \tag{5.19}$$

At lines 120 and 130 the conversion factors for discharge and head are evaluated as C1 and C2.

(3) In the loop between lines 210 and 260 values of Q and H are read in pairs from the data at lines 280 and 290 and the new pump's corresponding discharge and head values calculated and printed at line 250. The loop operates until all N pairs of data have been read and operated on.

(4) The table of results represents the characteristics of the larger pump. If the efficiency of the new pump was required this could readily be obtained by shifting the original pump Q-values to the new pump Q-values while the value of efficiency for each particular discharge remains unaltered.

PROBLEMS

(5.1) When a test on a hydraulic machine is carried out the analysis of the experimental data often requires both that individual machine characteristics be evaluated (as in Example 5.1) and that such characteristics be non-dimensionalised as presented in Example 5.2 so that the performance of pumps geometrically similar to that under test may be assessed.

Write a program that combines the essential elements of Examples 5.1 and 5.2 to yield both dimensioned and non-dimensional characteristics of the machines under investigation.

(5.2) While the use of dimensionless characteristics as a basis for the comparison of the performance of geometrically similar machines is a satisfactory concept, it does lack a certain brevity when the performance of different families of machines requires assessment. Such assessment is achieved by the use of the machine's type number or specific speed as explained in Section 5.4 and by Equations (5.9) and (5.10). In order to be able to compare machines of different type, write a program capable of evaluating specific speeds for pumps and turbines using the following examples to test the program.

Pumps

	Speed (rev/min)	Head (m)	Discharge (m³ /s)
Centrifugal	750	35	0.50
Axial	1450	4.0	0.090

Turbines

	Speed (rev/min)	Head (m)	Power developed (kW)
Pelton wheel	400	700	125
Francis	250	500	10000
Kaplan	140	100	2100

The data given above apply to the machine design points. The program should include as output an indication of the units of the parameters used in forming the specific speed. It should be clear that comparison is only possible between machine types if a consistent set of units is used throughout. It is suggested that speed should be expressed in rev/s or rad/s, head in metres, discharge in cubic metres/s and power output in watts.

The program output should indicate that the specific speed of the Kaplan turbine is greater than that of the Francis which itself is bigger than that of the Pelton wheel. The centrifugal pump type number will lie in the Pelton/Francis range while the axial flow pump will lie nearer the Kaplan value.

(5.3) When a given single pump is not capable of meeting the requirements of a given system it may be necessary to use a combination of pumps. Thus, if insufficient head is available from a single machine, a pair of these pumps in series could provide the required lift as explained in Section 5.5.

Develop a program capable of outputting the resultant characteristics from various combinations of machine. It is suggested that the program should initially be able to combine a pair of identical pumps in series and in parallel. The program could then be developed to combine machines of different characteristics. It may then be desirable to extend the program to afford the possibility of combining more than two machines (e.g. two in parallel, plus a third machine in series).

Test the program using data given below relating to two different centrifugal pumps.

Pump 1

Discharge (m³/s)	Head (m)
0	80
0.20	75
0.30	66
0.40	55
0.50	40
0.60	14

Pump 2

Discharge (m³/s)	Head (m)
0	100
0.05	98
0.10	95
0.15	85
0.20	59
0.25	6

(5.4) Example 5.3 involves the evaluation of the system characteristic that is to be matched with the pump characteristic. At line 90 in the program an input of friction factor is required. This is arrived at by estimating the value from the Moody diagram (Figure 3.3). Later in the program, at line 320, the decision whether or not to proceed with further iteration depends on the operator manually checking the latest friction factor value by calculating flow Reynolds number, etc.

Streamline the program of Example 5.3 in such a way that friction factor may be evaluated automatically by using either Moody's Equation (3.14) or the Colebrook–White Equation (3.15). The modified program should also check whether the solution has converged (i.e. that the most recent solution is the best).

(5.5) When establishing the operating point of a machine or combination of machines it is essential to know the details of the pipe system to which they are to be matched. In Example 5.3 the system resistance as expressed by Equation (5.11) is solely due to friction in the pipes. Generally, though, system resistance will have its source in not only friction but in other features such as bends, changes in cross-section, etc.

In order to be able to assess the value of K in Equation (5.11), develop a program capable of summing all the contributions to resistance from all sources so that the system characteristic may be formed. When this is done the program should calculate and output values of head and discharge for the system for given values of flow.

As an example with which to test the program, consider a pipe system which, on the suction side of a centrifugal pump, has an abrupt entrance to the pipe which is of diameter 0.2 m, length 3 m and friction factor 0.004. On the delivery side the pipe is of diameter 0.25 m, overall length 70 m and friction factor 0.003. There are two 45° elbows in the pipe (for which the local loss coefficient may be taken as 0.4) and the pipe terminates in an abrupt exit into a reservoir.

The static lift of the system is 10 m. Evaluate the system characteristic in the range up to 0.5 m³/s. (It may be possible to incorporate the loss directory, Example 3.2, in the program).

(5.6) It is not only important that the head and discharge for a pump be established by matching the machine to the pipe system but also that the efficiency of the whole system when at this operating point be reasonably high and that the input power requirements for the pump be met.

In Example 5.3 a problem is presented which requires the evaluation of operating point. If the variation of efficiency with discharge for this pump can be approximated by a parabola of equation

$$90 - \eta = 5.76 \times 10^5 \, (Q - 0.0125)^2 \qquad (5.20)$$

(where η is efficiency percent and Q is discharge in m³/s), modify the program in such a way that, for the given operating point the pump efficiency and hence the power input requirement may be found.

(5.7) Suggest how the problems posed in Example 5.3 and Problem 5.6 may be solved if, instead of having machine characteristics expressed by mathematical functions, information is available in the form of experimental data.

Investigate whether a satisfactory solution may be achieved for these problems if machine data, for Example 5.3, are expressed as follows

Discharge (m³/s)	Head (m)	Efficiency (%)
0	8	0
0.0025	7.96	32.4
0.005	7.84	57.6
0.0075	7.63	75.6
0.010	7.33	86.4
0.0125	6.93	90
0.0150	6.40	86.4
0.0175	5.71	75.6
0.020	4.80	57.6
0.0225	3.49	32.4
0.025	0	0

Data for the pipe system are as given previously.

(5.8) As indicated in Section 5.6, if the total head generated by a pump is H then, to avoid cavitation, only a head below the nett positive suction head, NPSH, should be on the suction side of the pump.

Thoma suggested that NPSH is proportional to H and defined a cavitation coefficient, the Thoma number

$$\sigma_{Th} = NPSH/H \tag{5.21}$$

Suction specific speed S_s is a parameter analogous to specific speed or type number discussed in Section 5.4 and is defined as

$$S_s = \frac{NQ^{1/2}}{(g\,NPSH)^{3/4}} \tag{5.22}$$

where N is rotational speed in rev/s, Q is discharge in m^3/s and NPSH is in metres.

Division of Equation (5.9) by (5.22) gives

$$\sigma_{Th} = (n_{SP}/S_s)^{4/3} \tag{5.23}$$

Starting from this relationship, develop a program which can be used to calculate the position of a pump relative to its datum level to avoid cavitation.

To test the program, consider a centrifugal pump of specific speed (based on rev/s) 0.07 which is required to pump water to a total head of 150 m from a lake. The vapour head of the water taken in by the pump is 0.03 m. The pump has a Thoma number of 0.072 and atmospheric pressure may be taken as being equivalent to 10.34 m of water.

Show that the pump should be below the free water surface of the lake (which should be taken as datum) to avoid cavitation.

The program should, of course, be capable of handling similar problems to that given above with only minor modifications to input requirements.

Chapter 6
Seepage and groundwater flow

ESSENTIAL THEORY

6.1 Introduction

Seepage is that flow which takes place through the small pores existing between particles that make up a soil. The forces exerted by such flows can be immense — sufficient to cause the collapse of mountainsides and destroy engineering works. It is essential that, for the successful operation of a vast spectrum of engineering schemes, the nature of such flows be known and controlled so as to eliminate the possibility of serious failure. Seepage flow is important in fields such as the design of dams and the construction of trenches, in the realisation of efficient drainage schemes and in the estimation of the water supply potential of a particular area. In this chapter the basic flow equations are presented together with some indications as to how they may be solved.

6.2 Soil permeability

The rate at which water flows through a soil depends on the available head and the nature of the soil. A material property called coefficient of permeability k, defined by Darcy in 1856, relates flow velocity v, to head gradient dh/dx, by the equation (in one dimension)

$$v = -k \frac{dh}{dx} \tag{6.1}$$

The coefficient of permeability accounts for differences in soil porosity, the shape and arrangement of the soil particles and the degree of saturation of the soil.

Several empirical relationships for the estimation of permeability have been proposed. That due to Hazen, applicable to homogeneous rounded grain media of not too fine a size, is of the form

$$k = C d_{10}^2 \, \text{m/s} \tag{6.2}$$

where d_{10} is the grain size in mm where 10% of the material is finer and

124

C is a constant in the range 0.010 to 0.015. Typical ranges for the permeability of different materials are given below.

Soil type	$k(m/s)$
Gravel	$>10^{-2}$
Clean sand	10^{-2} to 10^{-5}
Silt	10^{-5} to 10^{-8}
Fissured clay	10^{-4} to 10^{-8}
Intact clay	$<10^{-8}$

6.3 Measurement of permeability

In the laboratory, permeability is measured by means of a permeameter. A constant head instrument is used for material of relatively high permeability as shown in Figure 6.1, while for material of low permeability a falling head permeameter is used (Figure 6.2). In the first case permeability is given by

$$k = LQ/A\,\Delta H \tag{6.3}$$

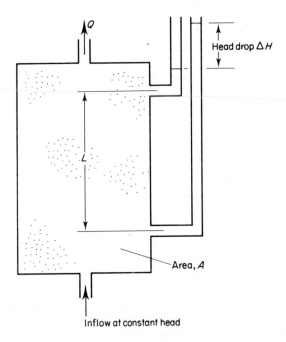

Figure 6.1 Constant head permeameter

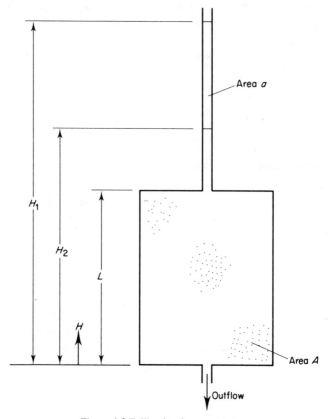

Figure 6.2 Falling head permeameter

where a steady flow of water Q passes through a sample of length L and cross-sectional area A across which the head drop is ΔH. In the second system permeability is given by

$$k = \frac{aL}{At} \ln \left(\frac{H_1}{H_2}\right) \tag{6.4}$$

where the head of water contained in a reservoir of cross-sectional area a falls from H_1 to H_2 in a time t, the water passing through the sample of length L and area A.

Because of problems associated with the use of possibly unrepresentative or disturbed samples of soil in the laboratory, *in situ* permeability tests are carried out. The most usual test method is the well-discharge technique which can be adopted in both unconfined and confined water-bearing strata (aquifers) as shown in Figure 6.3(a) and (b). In this method a well is sunk into the aquifer and water is pumped out at a constant rate. The piezometric surface (the head of the water in the aquifer) is lowered, a hydraulic gradient results and water flows towards the well. By monitoring the piezometric surface level at a pair of observation wells at different distances from the discharging well, an

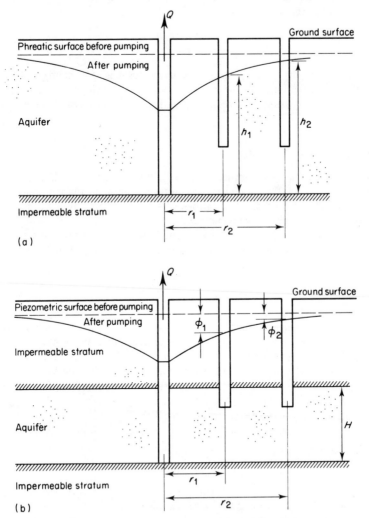

Figure 6.3(a) Pumping test in unconfined aquifer (*b*) Pumping test in confined aquifer

estimate of permeability may be made. With reference to the notation of Figure 6.3(a), the Dupuit formula for permeability is

$$k = \frac{Q \ln (r_2/r_1)}{\pi (h_2^2 - h_1^2)} \tag{6.5}$$

For a confined aquifer and referring to Figure 6.2(b), Thiem's formula for permeability is

$$k = \frac{Q \ln (r_2/r_1)}{2\pi H(\phi_1 - \phi_2)} \tag{6.6}$$

Other field permeability measurement techniques, for example those using a single borehole or those in which the velocity of a tracer chemical is measured between observation wells are beyond the scope of this book.

6.4 Flow nets

For a soil of known permeability it is important to be able to assess the quantity of flow and the distribution of head in the material. To accomplish this, the basic equations of flow must be solved for a wide variety of different flow geometries.

The analysis of a small two-dimensional fluid element leads to an equation in a quantity known as the stream function ψ, of the form

$$\frac{\partial^2 \psi}{\partial x^2} + \frac{\partial^2 \psi}{\partial y^2} = 0 \tag{6.7}$$

This is Laplace's equation. A similar equation can be obtained for a quantity known as the velocity potential function ϕ. When these equations are solved and the functions ψ and ϕ are plotted on the $x-y$ plane they form a set of orthogonal lines which furnish a description of the flow. Lines of constant ψ are streamlines and show the path which a fluid particle follows. Lines of constant ϕ are equipotential lines and indicate the distribution of head throughout the system.

In the context of seepage flow, potential function is related to head by the equation

$$\phi = -kh \tag{6.8}$$

while volume flow rate can be inferred from the difference between the numerical values attached to the streamlines.

The resultant mesh of stream- and headlines is termed a flow net and, in conjunction with Darcy's Law, can be used to estimate seepage flow rates, head distributions and forces on structures, etc. A simple

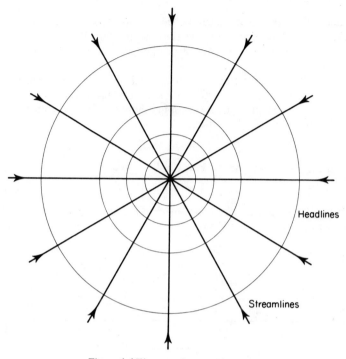

Figure 6.4 Flow-net for pumping test

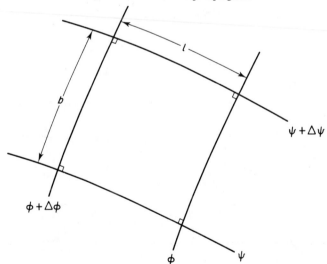

Figure 6.5 Element of flow-net

example of a flow net is that provided by the well-discharge technique of Figure 6.2. The corresponding flow net is shown in Figure 6.4 in which headlines are circles centred on the well and stream-lines are the radial lines.

In order to use the flow net for calculation purposes it is usual to keep the difference between head- and streamline values constant. Thus, for the element of mesh shown in Figure 6.5 for unit thickness of flow, Darcy's Law may be written

$$\Delta q = -bk\Delta h/L \qquad (6.9)$$

and with $\Delta q = \Delta \psi$ and $\Delta \phi = -k\Delta h$ this becomes

$$\Delta \psi = (b/L)\Delta \phi \qquad (6.10)$$

Thus, if $\Delta \psi$ and $\Delta \phi$ are constant then b/L is constant and may be chosen as unity so that the flow net is made up of curvilinear squares

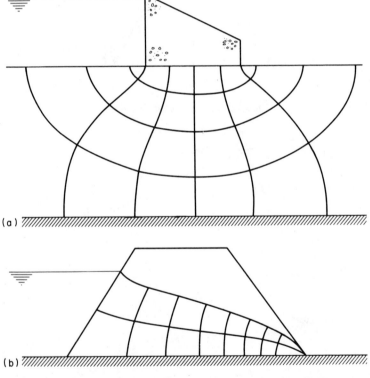

(a)

(b)

Figure 6.6(a) Flow-net for seepage under concrete dam (*b*) Flow-net for seepage through earth bank

which are reduced in area in regions of high head gradient (in Figure 6.4 this is close to the well).

Flow net solutions are generally arrived at by drawing a scale diagram of the system, fixing boundary stream- and headlines, sketching a few trial stream- and headlines and adjusting their position until all internal and external conditions are satisfied. There may be difficulty in establishing boundary streamlines in some examples of unconfined seepage. In such cases the position of these lines may be estimated and adjusted as for the internal lines of the net.

The graphical flow net solutions for seepage flow under an impermeable dam and through an earth embankment are shown in Figures 6.6(a) and (b). From Darcy's Law, flow per metre width is given by

$$Q = kH(N_f/N_e) \tag{6.11}$$

where N_f is the number of flow passages, N_e the number of equal head drops in the mesh and H is the total head difference across the system. The finer the mesh the better the estimate of the ratio N_f/N_e.

In regions of high head gradient and consequently high flow velocities (at the heel and toe of the dam in Figure 6.6(a)) washing out of material may be a problem causing instability and possible structural failure. The critical hydraulic gradient, i_c, that causes this quicksand condition is given by

$$i_c = (S - 1)/(1 + \eta) \tag{6.12}$$

where S is the soil specific gravity and η is soil porosity.

6.5 Numerical solution of seepage problems

In order to obtain a more detailed assessment of seepage flows, numerical methods for the solution of Laplace's equation based on the calculus of the finite differences may be used.

Solutions are usually achieved by assuming a network of ψ or ϕ lines and then adjusting these values systematically so that Laplace's equation and the appropriate boundary conditions are satisfied. If a square mesh is superimposed on the flow area and values of ψ are assigned to the nodes as in Figure 6.7, these values can be amended in sequence by assuming that the value of ψ at the central node 0 is the average of the ψ-values at the four surrounding nodes

$$\psi_0 = \frac{1}{4} (\psi_1 + \psi_2 + \psi_3 + \psi_4) \tag{6.13}$$

If a node is near a boundary then the distance from the central node to the four surrounding nodes will not be the same in each case.

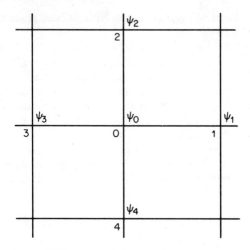

Figure 6.7 Square mesh for relaxation calculations

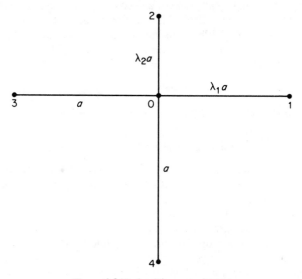

Figure 6.8 Mesh with unequal arms

Nodes nearer the central node 0 will influence the value at the centre more than those at a greater distance. For the example of Figure 6.8 with two unequal arms

$$\psi_0 = \frac{\psi_1/\lambda_1 + \psi_2/\lambda_2 + \psi_3 + \psi_4}{1/\lambda_1 + 1/\lambda_2 + 2} \qquad (6.14)$$

Example 6.1 WELLDRAWD: well discharge test in unconfined aquifer   133

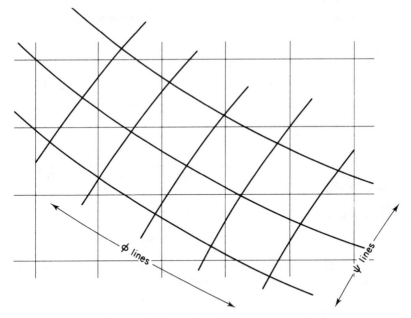

Figure 6.9 Flow-net superimposed on calculation mesh

when this relaxation process is complete, lines of constant ψ may be sketched on the grid and the flow net solution completed by adding orthogonal headlines as in Figure 6.9. Evaluation of discharges, forces and head gradients can then proceed as previously described.

WORKED EXAMPLES

Example 6.1 WELLDRAWD: well discharge test in unconfined aquifer

A laboratory experiment to establish the permeability of a sample of sand was conducted in a tank containing a model well and a series of piezometer tubes. The sand was saturated with water until all the piezometers registered a height of 0.20 m above the flat base of the tank as shown in Figure 6.10. In order to achieve a state of dynamic equilibrium in the tank an inflow of water was provided at the ends of the tank to compensate for the water being extracted via the model well. Any excess inflow was removed by overflow pipes as indicated in the Figure. The withdrawal of water from the well caused a flow towards the extraction point and a consequent depression in the piezometric heights. When these levels were steady they were noted together with

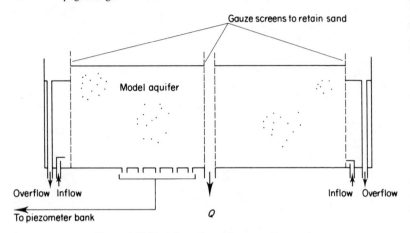

Figure 6.10 Model aquifer and seepage flow tank

the volume flow rate from the well. For piezometers spaced at 100 mm intervals from the well centre the readings were

Distance from well (mm)	Piezometer height (m)
100	0.100
200	0.145
300	0.166
400	0.179
500	0.189

This set of data was obtained for a discharge of three litres per minute (5.10^{-5} m^3/s).

Write a program to evaluate the coefficient of permeability of the sand in the tank.

```
LIST

WELLDRAWD  6-JUL-81  09:40:17

10 PRINT "WELL DRAW-DOWN ANALYSIS - UNCONFINED AQUIFER"
20 DIM R(10),H(10),K(10)
30 DATA 100,0.1,200,0.145,300,0.166,400,0.179,500,0.189
35 PRINT
40 PRINT "HOW MANY PAIRS OF DATA POINTS?    ";
50 INPUT N
60 PRINT
70 PRINT "WELL DISCHARGE (CUMECS)?    ";
80 INPUT Q
90 PRINT
100 PRINT "R1","H1","R2","H2","K"
110 PRINT "MM","M","MM","M","M/S"
120 PRINT "----------------------------------------------------------------
130 READ R(1),H(1)
```

Example 6.1 WELLDRAWD: well discharge test in unconfined aquifer   135

```
140 FOR I=2 TO N
150 READ R(I),H(I)
160 K(I-1)=Q*LOG(R(I)/R(I-1))/(PI*(H(I)^2-H(I-1)^2))
170 PRINT R(I-1),H(I-1),R(I),H(I),K(I-1)
180 NEXT I
190 PRINT
200 T=0
210 FOR J=1 TO N-1
220 T=T+K(J)
230 NEXT J
240 A=T/(N-1)
250 PRINT "AVERAGE VALUE OF PERMEABILITY IS",A,"M/S"
260 END

READY


RUN

WELLDRAWD  6-JUL-81  09:40:50

WELL DRAW-DOWN ANALYSIS - UNCONFINED AQUIFER

HOW MANY PAIRS OF DATA POINTS?   ? 5

WELL DISCHARGE (CUMECS)?   ? 0.00005

R1              H1              R2              H2              K
MM              M               MM              M               M/S
--------------------------------------------------------------------------
100             .1              200             .145            1.00062E-03
200             .145            300             .166            9.88084E-04
300             .166            400             .179            1.02087E-03
400             .179            500             .189            9.65066E-04

AVERAGE VALUE OF PERMEABILITY IS                9.93659E-04  M/S

READY
```

Program notes

(1) The data for the particular experiment in what is a model of an unconfined aquifer, are input in pairs at line 30 and the number of such pairs and the discharge are input in response to the prompts at lines 50 and 80 as N and Q respectively.

(2) Following the printing of the headings and units of the required output at lines 110–130 the problem is initiated by reading the first pair of data points as R(1) and H(1).

(3) Evaluation of permeability K is to be undertaken for (in this case) adjacent pairs of piezometer readings. This allows four estimates of K to be made from the 5 data points. In the loop between lines 150 and 190, pairs of data points are read and, together with the previously read pair, are substituted into Equation (6.5) to evaluate K. The values of R and H used in deriving this K value are then printed at line 180.

(4) In order to assess the average value from these calculations the loop between lines 220 and 240 sums up the available (N−1) K-values and at line 250 the average is calculated as A and printed at line 260.

Example 6.2 CASAGRAND: seepage surface in earth dam

The construction of a flow net for the estimation of seepage flow through a permeable embankment is complicated by the fact that the boundary streamline from the free water surface to the downstream side of the dam (the line of saturation or phreatic line) cannot be positioned exactly prior to the commencement of flow net construction. In order to ease the problem, Casagrande proposed a method whereby the central portion of this streamline could be positioned reliably leaving only the extremities to be estimated.

The method involves the construction of a parabola with its focus at the toe of the embankment E in Figure 6.11 of equation

$$x = (y^2 - x_0^2)/2x_0 \qquad (6.15)$$

where x_0 is found by swinging an arc centre E through F to meet AE at G and measuring along AE to I vertically below F. The parabola passes through D at a distance $x_0/2$ from E and through F which is 0.3 times distance AH from B. The program below derives the coordinates of the parabola (with respect to the axes shown in the Figure) thus enabling the boundary streamline to be sketched as indicated.

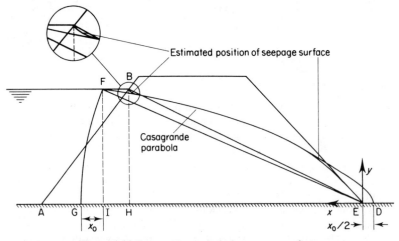

Figure 6.11 Casagrande parabola for seepage surface

```
LIST

CASAGRAND   6-JUL-81   09:43:40

10 PRINT "CASAGRANDE CONSTRUCTION FOR UNCONFINED SEEPAGE"
20 PRINT "----------------------------------------------"
30 DIM Y(50),X(50)
40 PRINT
```

Example 6.2 CASAGRAND: seepage surface in earth dam   137

```
50 PRINT "HEAD OF WATER BEHIND BANK (M)=   ";
60 INPUT H
70 PRINT "SLOPE OF WETTED SIDE (DEGREES)=   ";
80 INPUT A1
90 A=PI*A1/180
100 T=SIN(A)/COS(A)
110 PRINT "LENGTH OF BASE (M)=   ";
120 INPUT B
130 C=.3*H*(1/T)
140 D1=(B-H*(1/T))^2
150 D=SQR(H*H+D1)
160 E=ATN(B/H-1/T)
170 F=SQR(C*C+D*D+2*C*D*SIN(E))
180 G=F-SQR(F*F-H*H)
190 PRINT
200 PRINT "C","D","E","F","G"
210 PRINT "----------------------------------------------------------------"
220 PRINT C,D,E,F,G
230 PRINT
240 PRINT
250 PRINT "HOW MANY STEPS?   ";
260 INPUT N
270 PRINT
280 S=H/N
290 PRINT "X","Y"
300 PRINT "-------------------------"
310 Y(1)=0
320 PRINT -G/2,Y(1)
330 FOR I=2 TO N+1
340 Y(I)=Y(I-1)+S
350 X(I)=(Y(I)*Y(I)-G*G)/(2*G)
360 PRINT X(I),Y(I)
370 NEXT I
380 END

READY


RUN


CASAGRAND  6-JUL-81  09:44:25

CASAGRANDE CONSTRUCTION FOR UNCONFINED SEEPAGE
------------------------------------------------

HEAD OF WATER BEHIND BANK (M)=   ? 10
SLOPE OF WETTED SIDE (DEGREES)=   ? 45
LENGTH OF BASE (M)=   ? 30
```

C	D	E	F	G
3	22.3607	1.10715	25.0799	2.07987

```
HOW MANY STEPS?   ? 40
```

X	Y
-1.03994	0
-1.02491	.25
-.979836	.5
-.904711	.75
-.799537	1
-.664312	1.25
-.499037	1.5
-.303713	1.75
-.0783385	2
.177086	2.25
.46256	2.5

.778084	2.75
1.12366	3
1.49928	3.25
1.90496	3.5
2.34068	3.75
2.80645	4
3.30228	4.25
3.82815	4.5
4.38408	4.75
4.97005	5
5.58607	5.25
6.23215	5.5
6.90827	5.75
7.61444	6
8.35067	6.25
9.11694	6.5
9.91326	6.75
10.7396	7
11.5961	7.25
12.4825	7.5
13.3991	7.75
14.3456	8
15.3222	8.25
16.3289	8.5
17.3656	8.75
18.4324	9
19.5292	9.25
20.6561	9.5
21.813	9.75
23	10

READY

Program notes

(1) In response to the prompts between lines 50 and 120 the basic geometry of the problem is input. (The slope of the wetted bank is input in degrees and converted to radians at line 90, the tangent of the slope is found at line 100.)

(2) Between lines 130 and 180 the dimensions that are required for the valuation of x_0 (GI) are calculated (C is FB, D is BE, E is angle HBE, F is FE evaluated from the cosine rule and G is x_0). These quantities are printed at line 220 to allow some check on their magnitude to be made if required.

(3) With the important length x_0 evaluated it is now possible to calculate points on the parabola and in response to the prompt at line 250 the number of increments in the y-direction is input and after printing the initial x and y values at line 320 as $(x_0/2, 0)$ the loop between 330 and 370 evaluates the x-values corresponding to the selected y-values by substitution into the rearranged Casagrande parabola equation. Each successive pair is tabulated enabling the seepage surface parabola to be drawn on the dam as indicated in the Figure. The extremes of the seepage surface require estimation: on the upstream face at B the streamline leaves at $90°$ while on the downstream slope the line fairs into the dam surface as indicated. The flow-net can now be constructed as indicated in the text.

Example 6.3 MESHRELAX: relaxation of square mesh   139

Example 6.3 MESHRELAX: relaxation of square mesh

It is required that the seepage flow beneath a concrete dam be estimated by the development of a flow-net derived from the relaxation of a mesh of assumed stream-function values. The dam is built on a permeable soil which is wholly contained within an impermeable rock basin as shown in Figure 6.12. There is a 10 m head of water behind the

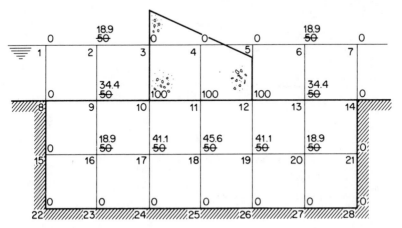

Figure 6.12 Relaxed mesh for seepage under concrete dam

dam which is 20 m wide at the base. The mesh is square of side 10 m. The first stage in the production of the flow net is to assign arbitrary values to the nodal points of the mesh. These values will be constant at the rock/soil interface (and set equal to zero) and at the soil/dam interface where they are set at 100. These constant valued boundaries represent the boundary streamlines of the flow. The remaining nodes are assigned arbitrary values – here, for convenience, all are set at 50. In order that the soil/water interface node values (9 and 13) can be relaxed it is useful to introduce 'dummy' nodes 2 and 6 which always have the same nodal value as nodes 16 and 20 directly below 9 and 13.

The procedure now is to systematically adjust internal node values using Equation (6.13) since all mesh arms are equal here. The following program is used to adjust the node values until Equation (6.13) is satisfied.

```
LIST

MESHRELAX  6-JUL-81  09:51:06

10 PRINT "RELAXATION OF SQUARE MESH"
20 PRINT
30 DIM V(100),N(100),B(100)
40 PRINT "NUMBER OF NODES IN MESH= ";
```

```
50 INPUT C
60 DATA 0,50,0,0,0,50,0
70 DATA 0,50,100,100,100,50,0
80 DATA 0,50,50,50,50,50,0
90 DATA 0,0,0,0,0,0,0
100 FOR I=1 TO C
110 READ V(I)
120 NEXT I
130 PRINT "NUMBER OF NODES TO ADJUST=    ";
140 INPUT N
150 PRINT "NUMBER OF THESE NODES"
160 PRINT "------------------------"
170 FOR I=8 TO C
180 IF V(I)=0 GO TO 230
190 IF V(I)=100 GO TO 230
200 PRINT I
210 B(I)=(V(I-7)+V(I+1)+V(I+7)+V(I-1))/4
220 V(I)=B(I)
230 NEXT I
240 PRINT
250 PRINT "NODE NUMBER","RELAXED VALUE"
260 PRINT "-----------------------------"
270 V(2)=V(16)
280 V(6)=V(20)
290 FOR I=1 TO C
300 PRINT I,V(I)
310 NEXT I
320 PRINT
330 PRINT "ANY FURTHER RELAXATION CYCLES REQUIRED? (Y/N)";
340 INPUT A$
350 IF A$="N" THEN 380
360 PRINT
370 GO TO 150
380 END

READY



RUN


MESHRELAX   6-JUL-81   09:51:44

RELAXATION OF SQUARE MESH

NUMBER OF NODES IN MESH= ? 28
NUMBER OF NODES TO ADJUST=    ? 7
NUMBER OF THESE NODES
--------------------------
  9
 13
 16
 17
 18
 19
 20

NODE NUMBER    RELAXED VALUE
------------------------------
  1            0
  2            25
  3            0
  4            0
  5            0
  6            24.9023
  7            0
  8            0
  9            50
 10            100
 11            100
```

Example 6.3 MESHRELAX: relaxation of square mesh   141

```
12            100
13            50
14            0
15            0
16            25
17            43.75
18            48.4375
19            49.6094
20            24.9023
21            0
22            0
23            0
24            0
25            0
26            0
27            0
28            0
```

ANY FURTHER RELAXATION CYCLES REQUIRED? (Y/N)? Y

NUMBER OF THESE NODES

```
9
13
16
17
18
19
20
```

NODE NUMBER   RELAXED VALUE

```
1             0
2             18.9167
3             0
4             0
5             0
6             18.8924
7             0
8             0
9             34.4883
10            100
11            100
12            100
13            34.4519
14            0
15            0
16            18.9167
17            41.1296
18            45.5671
19            41.1177
20            18.8924
21            0
22            0
23            0
24            0
25            0
26            0
27            0
28            0
```

ANY FURTHER RELAXATION CYCLES REQUIRED? (Y/N)? Y

NUMBER OF THESE NODES

```
9
13
16
17
18
19
20
```

```
NODE NUMBER    RELAXED VALUE
----------------------------------
   1            0
   2           18.897
   3            0
   4            0
   5            0
   6           18.8897
   7            0
   8            0
   9           34.4584
  10          100
  11          100
  12          100
  13           34.4462
  14            0
  15            0
  16           18.897
  17           41.116
  18           45.5584
  19           41.1127
  20           18.8897
  21            0
  22            0
  23            0
  24            0
  25            0
  26            0
  27            0
  28            0

ANY FURTHER RELAXATION CYCLES REQUIRED? (Y/N)? N

READY
```

Program notes

(1) In order to ease the problems of mesh annotation the grid super-imposed on the seepage zone extends for one square above the ground level in order to include 'dummy' or 'mirror-image' nodes 2 and 6 which will have the same node values after (and during) relaxation as nodes 16 and 20. Thus, in data at line 60 node 2 and node 6 are given the same initial value of 50 as 16 and 20. All other nodes 1, 3–5 and 7 are set to zero. They will not be operated on but are required to facilitate calculation of other values.

(2) After reading the C values of data the N nodes that are to be adjusted in value are identified in the loop beginning at line 170. The running variable I goes from 8 to C because the first 7 nodes are essentially outside the field of the problem, as described above. Having identified a node requiring adjustment the node number is printed and, by using Equation (6.13) the relaxed value B(I) is obtained. This value is stored as a new V(I) value at line 220.

(3) The relaxed nodal values are now to be output under the heading at line 250. First, though, to ensure that the two dummy nodes are assigned the correct value for succeeding iterations, lines 270 and 280 are included before the node number and current value are printed.

(4) In response to the prompt at line 330 the relaxation procedure can

Example 6.4 INTERPOLN: estimation of streamline positions   143

be reinitiated or ended depending on the form of the input at line 340. The output shows the results of the first, sixth and seventh iteration (after which an acceptable convergence has been obtained). The following Example 6.4 demonstrates how the flow net construction may be completed.

Example 6.4 INTERPOLN: estimation of streamline positions

The previous example of mesh relaxation yielded nodal values of stream function that satisfied Equation (6.13). The relaxed mesh values are shown in Figure 6.13. In order to complete the construction of the flow net to evaluate (for example) the quantity of seepage flow it is necessary initially to plot the streamline trajectories over the relaxed mesh. The simple program given below will obtain the point of inter-section of a streamline of selected value with the mesh lines from which the flow net may be constructed as described in the program notes.

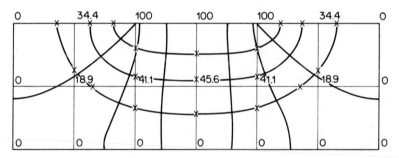

Figure 6.13 Completed flow-net for seepage under concrete dam

```
LIST

INTERPOLN   6-JUL-81   10:01:15

10 PRINT "INTERPOLATION OF RELAXED MESH STREAM FUNCTION VALUES"
20 PRINT
30 PRINT "STANDARD MESH SIZE= ";
40 INPUT L
50 PRINT
60 PRINT "VALUE OF STREAM LINE (PSI) =";
70 INPUT S
80 PRINT
90 PRINT "NODAL VALUES FOR INTERPOLATION ARE    ";
100 INPUT A,B
110 PRINT
120 PRINT "IS DISTANCE BETWEEN MESH POINTS STANDARD? (Y/N)";
130 INPUT A$
140 PRINT
150 IF A$="N" GO TO 180
160 X=L*ABS((S-A)/(A-B))
170 GO TO 220
180 PRINT "DISTANCE BETWEEN MESH POINTS=";
190 INPUT D
```

```
200 PRINT
210 X=D*ABS((S-A)/(A-B))
220 PRINT "DISTANCE FROM FIRST MESH NUMBER INPUT TO LINE =  ";
230 PRINT X
240 PRINT
250 PRINT "ANY FURTHER DATA FOR THIS STREAMLINE VALUE? (Y/N)";
260 INPUT B$
270 PRINT
280 IF B$="Y" GO TO 90
290 PRINT "IS STREAM LINE VALUE TO BE ALTERED (Y/N)";
300 INPUT C$
310 PRINT
320 IF C$="Y" GO TO 30
330 END

READY


RUN


INTERPOLN  6-JUL-81  10:01:52

INTERPOLATION OF RELAXED MESH STREAM FUNCTION VALUES

STANDARD MESH SIZE= ? 10

VALUE OF STREAM LINE (PSI) =? 75

NODAL VALUES FOR INTERPOLATION ARE   ? 34.4,100

IS DISTANCE BETWEEN MESH POINTS STANDARD? (Y/N)? Y

DISTANCE FROM FIRST MESH NUMBER INPUT TO LINE =   6.18902

ANY FURTHER DATA FOR THIS STREAMLINE VALUE? (Y/N)? Y

NODAL VALUES FOR INTERPOLATION ARE   ? 41.1,100

IS DISTANCE BETWEEN MESH POINTS STANDARD? (Y/N)? Y

DISTANCE FROM FIRST MESH NUMBER INPUT TO LINE =   5.75552

ANY FURTHER DATA FOR THIS STREAMLINE VALUE? (Y/N)? Y

NODAL VALUES FOR INTERPOLATION ARE   ? 45.6,100

IS DISTANCE BETWEEN MESH POINTS STANDARD? (Y/N)? Y

DISTANCE FROM FIRST MESH NUMBER INPUT TO LINE =   5.40441

ANY FURTHER DATA FOR THIS STREAMLINE VALUE? (Y/N)? Y

NODAL VALUES FOR INTERPOLATION ARE   ? 41.1,100

IS DISTANCE BETWEEN MESH POINTS STANDARD? (Y/N)? Y

DISTANCE FROM FIRST MESH NUMBER INPUT TO LINE =   5.75552

ANY FURTHER DATA FOR THIS STREAMLINE VALUE? (Y/N)? Y

NODAL VALUES FOR INTERPOLATION ARE   ? 34.4,100

IS DISTANCE BETWEEN MESH POINTS STANDARD? (Y/N)? Y

DISTANCE FROM FIRST MESH NUMBER INPUT TO LINE =   6.18902

ANY FURTHER DATA FOR THIS STREAMLINE VALUE? (Y/N)? N

IS STREAM LINE VALUE TO BE ALTERED (Y/N)? Y
```

Example 6.4 INTERPOLN: estimation of streamline positions   145

```
STANDARD MESH SIZE= ? 10

VALUE OF STREAM LINE (PSI) =? 50

NODAL VALUES FOR INTERPOLATION ARE    ? 34.4,100

IS DISTANCE BETWEEN MESH POINTS STANDARD? (Y/N)? Y

DISTANCE FROM FIRST MESH NUMBER INPUT TO LINE =   2.37805

ANY FURTHER DATA FOR THIS STREAMLINE VALUE? (Y/N)? Y

NODAL VALUES FOR INTERPOLATION ARE    ? 41.1,100

IS DISTANCE BETWEEN MESH POINTS STANDARD? (Y/N)? Y

DISTANCE FROM FIRST MESH NUMBER INPUT TO LINE =   1.51104

ANY FURTHER DATA FOR THIS STREAMLINE VALUE? (Y/N)? Y

NODAL VALUES FOR INTERPOLATION ARE    ? 45.6,100

IS DISTANCE BETWEEN MESH POINTS STANDARD? (Y/N)? Y

DISTANCE FROM FIRST MESH NUMBER INPUT TO LINE =   .808824

ANY FURTHER DATA FOR THIS STREAMLINE VALUE? (Y/N)? N

IS STREAM LINE VALUE TO BE ALTERED (Y/N)? Y

STANDARD MESH SIZE= ? 10

VALUE OF STREAM LINE (PSI) =? 25

NODAL VALUES FOR INTERPOLATION ARE    ? 0,34.4

IS DISTANCE BETWEEN MESH POINTS STANDARD? (Y/N)? Y

DISTANCE FROM FIRST MESH NUMBER INPUT TO LINE =   7.26744

ANY FURTHER DATA FOR THIS STREAMLINE VALUE? (Y/N)? Y

NODAL VALUES FOR INTERPOLATION ARE    ? 18.9,41.1

IS DISTANCE BETWEEN MESH POINTS STANDARD? (Y/N)? Y

DISTANCE FROM FIRST MESH NUMBER INPUT TO LINE =   2.74775

ANY FURTHER DATA FOR THIS STREAMLINE VALUE? (Y/N)? Y

NODAL VALUES FOR INTERPOLATION ARE    ? 0,41.1

IS DISTANCE BETWEEN MESH POINTS STANDARD? (Y/N)? Y

DISTANCE FROM FIRST MESH NUMBER INPUT TO LINE =   6.08273

ANY FURTHER DATA FOR THIS STREAMLINE VALUE? (Y/N)? Y

NODAL VALUES FOR INTERPOLATION ARE    ? 0,45.6

IS DISTANCE BETWEEN MESH POINTS STANDARD? (Y/N)? Y

DISTANCE FROM FIRST MESH NUMBER INPUT TO LINE =   5.48246

ANY FURTHER DATA FOR THIS STREAMLINE VALUE? (Y/N)? N

IS STREAM LINE VALUE TO BE ALTERED (Y/N)? N


READY
```

Program notes

(1) In response to the prompt at line 30 the size of the squares making up the mesh is input as L.

(2) From inspection of the boundary streamline values, the values of stream-function whose trajectories are to be plotted are decided upon and the first of these is input as S at line 70. The places where this streamline will cross the mesh lines are found from inspection of the relaxed mesh and the nodal values bounding the intersection point are input as A and B at line 100.

(3) A check is made to establish that the distance between the nodal values A and B is standard (L) and depending on the response made to line 120 the parameter X is evaluated where X is the distance from A to the intersection point. (If the distance is not standard, the new length is input at 190 following a negative response to 120.)

(4) The intersection distance is printed at X before the operator decides whether further data are to be processed for the particular streamline or whether the streamline value is now to be altered.

(5) The intersection points are now entered on the relaxed mesh and the streamline sketched in through these points. Streamlines corresponding to stream-function values of 75, 50 and 25 have been selected. It is now possible to draw in corresponding headlines ensuring that they everywhere intersect streamlines orthogonally and form a flow net consisting of curvilinear squares as shown in Figure 6.13.

(6) By using Equation (6.11) the discharge per metre width of dam can be evaluated. Here

$$N_f = 4, N_e = 8 \text{ and with } k = 10 \text{ m per day and } H = 10 \text{ m}$$
$$Q = \frac{4}{8} \times 10 \times 10 \text{ m}^3/\text{day per m width}$$
$$= 50 \text{ m}^3/\text{day per m width}$$

Example 6.5 UPLIFTFCE: calculation of uplift force on dam base

In the previous two examples the flow net for seepage under a concrete dam has been evaluated. It is often necessary to evaluate forces on structures such as dams, retaining walls, trench piles, etc. that are the result of such seepage flows. The following program is used to estimate the uplift force on the dam from the flow net of Figure 6.13.

```
LIST

UPLIFTFCE   6-JUL-81   10:07:23

10 PRINT "UPLIFT FORCE ON DAM FOUNDATIONS"
20 PRINT
30 DATA 7.5,6.25,5,3.75,2.5
40 DATA 5,5,5,5
```

Example 6.5 UPLIFTFCE: calculation of uplift force on dam base 147

```
50 PRINT 'NUMBER OF SURFACES ON WHICH PRESSURE ACTS=   ';
60 INPUT N
70 DIM H(100),X(100),F(100)
80 PRINT 'DENSITY OF SEEPING FLUID (KG/M^3)=   ';
90 INPUT D
100 FOR I=1 TO N
110 READ H(I)
120 NEXT I
130 FOR I=1 TO N+1
140 READ X(I)
150 NEXT I
160 F(0)=0
170 FOR I=1 TO N
180 F(I)=F(I-1)+(D*9.81*(H(I)+H(I+1))/2)*X(I)
190 NEXT I
195 R=F(N)/1000
200 PRINT
210 PRINT 'UPLIFT FORCE ON DAM IS',R,'KN PER METRE WIDTH'
220 END

READY


RUN

UPLIFTFCE   6-JUL-81   10:07:50

UPLIFT FORCE ON DAM FOUNDATIONS

NUMBER OF SURFACES ON WHICH PRESSURE ACTS=   ? 4
DENSITY OF SEEPING FLUID (KG/M^3)=   ? 1000

UPLIFT FORCE ON DAM IS        751.078      KN PER METRE WIDTH

READY
```

Program notes

(1) From the flow net the values of headline along the base of the dam are read and entered as data at line 30. The distances between these headlines along the dam base are measured and entered as data at line 40.

(2) In response to the prompt at line 50 the number of these distances (referred to as surfaces on which pressure acts) is entered as N. The DIM statement at line 70 creates up to 100 spaces for storage of the head, distance and force parameters. Seeping fluid density is input as D at line 90.

(3) In the two loops, lines 100 to 120 and 130 to 150 the data are read in two sets as H(I) and X(I).

(4) After initialising the force calculation at line 160 the loop between lines 170 and 190 evaluates uplift by averaging the value of head containing a given distance, multiplying this by density and gravitational acceleration to obtain pressure and then multiplying by X(I) to obtain force per metre width in this section. This is added to the sum of the forces on the previous surfaces to obtain a total upthrust.

(5) The resultant force R in kilonewtons is calculated at line 200 and printed at line 220.

PROBLEMS

(6.1) Write a program capable of analysing data from experiments conducted in laboratory permeameter tests.

The program should be able to handle data from both constant head instruments and from falling head devices and should have provision for inputting various different geometries, etc.

The program may be tested by showing that the permability of a soil sample measured by a constant head permeameter (Figure 6.1) of cylindrical cross-section (diameter 120 mm) containing a sample of length 500 mm, across which a head drop of 35 mm of water is maintained with a flow rate of 47.5 ml/minute is 10^{-3} m/s. Also, in a test using a falling head permeameter consisting of a cylindrical tube of uniform diameter 10 mm throughout, the head of water above a 20 mm thick plug of soil in the bottom of the cylinder fell from 300 mm to 100 mm in 1 h and the soil permeability was found to be 6.10^{-6} m/s.

(6.2) Example 6.2 presents a program for the evaluation of permeability in a well-discharge test in an unconfined aquifer. In the program, pairs of data from adjacent piezometers are used to evaluate permeability by using equation (6.5).

A better way of analysing the experimental information would be to take any pair of piezometer distances and heights from the results and evaluate permeability from Equation (6.5). Thus, for the five sets of data presented in Example 6.1 there are 10 different ways of choosing two pairs of data.

Modify the program of Example 6.1 in order to obtain as many estimates of permeability as the data allow by including not only calculations for adjacent pairs but also every other combination.

(6.3) Example 6.1 is concerned with the analysis of data from a well-discharge experiment in an unconfined aquifer. Extend the program of this example (perhaps modified in the way suggested in Problem (6.2)) so that data from experiments in confined aquifers may be analysed uisng Equation (6.5). To test the program use the data given in Example 6.1 with the additional information that the depth of the model aquifer may be taken as 0.140 m.

(6.4) The relaxation of a mesh as illustrated in Example 6.3 enables streamlines and orthogonal headlines to be sketched and a flow net constructed. In such an approach it is at no time necessary (or possible) to write down equations relating stream function or potential function to the space coordinates x and y. All that is required is that a value of head be assigned to the head-lines in the completed flow net if any forces are to be evaluated, etc.

However, it is sometimes desirable to represent such functions mathematically — there are many cases when complex systems may be idealised by the use of such functions not only in fluid mechanics but in other fields such as stress analysis, electricity and heat transfer. To illustrate this approach, consider a stream function

$$\psi = xy \qquad (6.16)$$

It can be shown that the corresponding orthogonal potential function ϕ is given by

$$\phi = \frac{1}{2}(x^2 - y^2) \qquad (6.17)$$

Remembering that the stream function is constant along a streamline and that potential function is constant along a headline, write a program to evaluate the two functions for selected constant values of ψ and ϕ in the top right and top left quadrants of the $x - y$ plane and, by plotting the output, show that such functions can represent the idealisation of the flow of fluid associated with a 90° corner or that associated with the impact of a jet on a plane wall.

(**6.5**) Examples 6.3 and 6.4 together present a pair of simple programs which assist in the construction of a flow net for seepage under a concrete dam. The mesh used in these examples is coarse, as is the resulting flow net. In order to investigate the improvement in the assessment of the quantity of seepage under the dam as expressed by Program Note (6) in Example 6.4, rerun the program suitably modified to incorporate a finer initial mesh than that shown in Figure 6.12. It is suggested that each square be split into 4 smaller squares thus increasing the number of nodes from 28 to 91. This will mean that a more accurate assessment of streamline positions may be made and indeed more streamlines may be drawn with confidence, leading to a more accurate estimate of the ratio N_f/N_e in Equation (6.11).

(**6.6**) The geometry of the dam and aquifer of Example 6.3 leads to a square mesh in which all arm lengths between nodes in Figure 6.12 are constant. When the geometry of a problem is such that the seepage area cannot be completely covered by a square mesh, some variation in the relaxation procedure will be required whereby a modified relaxation equation (such as Equation (6.14)) is applied appropriately.

Modify the program of Example 6.3 to include a facility whereby nodes surrounded by unequal arms may be relaxed using the correct relaxation relationship.

As an example with which to test any modification consider the dam of Figure 6.12 altered such that now the wetted face extends below the ground level to half-way between nodes 10 and 17 and then slopes up uniformly to meet node 12 at the toe of the dam. This results in nodes 17 and 18 being surrounded by arms that are not all equal. (Note that the dam/aquifer interface is still a boundary streamline and the value of the streamline is set at 100 here.)

(6.7) Write a program to facilitate the construction of a flow net for seepage flow beneath a sheet pile wall constructed in order to keep water out of a new dry dock facility. The depth of water behind the wall is 10 m and the pile extends 10 m into the aquifer of permeability 5m/day. At 10 m below the bottom of the wall there is a horizontal impervious layer of bedrock. On the 'dry' side of the wall the aquifer extends to 15 m above the bedrock (i.e. there is a difference of 5 m between the surface of the aquifer on either side of the wall). Any water that does seep into the dry dock is immediately pumped out. The program may be a modification of that in Example 6.3 and it would be useful if an interpolation scheme could be incorporated. (The seepage flow is estimated at 25 m³/day/m width.)

(6.8) The program presented in Example 6.5 for the evaluation of upthrust forces on the horizontal base of the dam of Figure 6.12 requires modification if the surfaces on which the pressure acts are inclined to the horizontal.

Alter the program of Example 6.5 so that the horizontal and vertical components of thrust acting on a structure subject to seepage flow forces may be evaluated. The geometry of Problem (6.6) may be used to test any modifications.

(6.9) The approach to the solution of seepage flow problems presented in the examples and extended in the foregoing problems is an elementary one. There are many sophistications that may be incorporated in any solution scheme.

It is usual and convenient to overlay a square mesh onto any particular problem geometry though the straight sides of the mesh will not generally coincide with the boundaries of the seepage zone.

Suggest ways in which a program may cope with deviations from exact correspondence of mesh and system boundaries with regard to the following.

(1) The square mesh is overlaid in such a way that entire squares are not included in the seepage zone. Nodes that form the corners of such squares will most likely be identified in the computation scheme even though they will not be operated on.

(2) The boundary of the seepage zone intersects the mesh in such a way that a node requiring relaxation may have up to three of the four surrounding nodes outside the boundary.

(3) The boundary of the seepage zone intersects the mesh as in (2). How are the nodes inside the boundary to be dealt with, remembering that there may be adjacent nodes to be relaxed?

(4) To speed up the relaxation procedure in a problem with an axis of symmetry (as in Figure 6.12), it is not necessary to relax all the nodes. How can such a curtailment of the calculation be realised?

Bibliography

In addition to those books listed in Section 1.5, the following are also suggested further reading.

Cedergren, H.R., *Seepage, Drainage and Flownets*, 2nd ed., Wiley, (1977).

Chow, V.T., *Open-Channel Hydraulics*, McGraw-Hill, (1959).

Douglas, J.F., Gasiorek, J.M., and Swaffield, J.A., *Fluid Mechanics*, Pitman, (1979).

Fox, J.A., *Hydraulic Analysis of Unsteady Flow in Pipe Networks*, MacMillan, (1977).

Lomax, W.R. and Saul, A.J., *Laboratory Work in Hydraulics*, Granada, (1979).

Massey, B.S., *Mechanics of Fluids*, 4th ed., Van Nostrand Reinhold, (1979).

Webber, *Fluid Mechanics for Civil Engineers*, SI ed., Chapman and Hall, (1971).

Wilson, *Engineering Hydrology*, 2nd ed., MacMillan, (1974).

Index